REPORT for DUTY

Lily A. Bear

Christian Light Publications, Inc.
Harrisonburg, Virginia 22802

REPORT FOR DUTY

Christian Light Publications, Inc., Harrisonburg, Virginia 22802
©2003 by Christian Light Publications, Inc.
All rights reserved. Published 2003
Printed in the United States of America

12 11 10 09 08 07 06 05 04 03   5 4 3 2 1

Cover Design: David W. Miller

ISBN 0-87813-610-X

Dedicated to—

Christian Youth

As they face the

Enemy,

Who tests their faithfulness

to God.

"I have no greater joy than to hear that my children walk in TRUTH" (3 John 4).

Preface

This is the true story of John M. Witmer of Ohio, who lived only 32 days after entering military camp. During WWI nearly all eligible men were drafted into the army, even though they had registered as conscientious objectors.

The Columbiana Post Office opened and censored all mail sent to or from military camps. Several local ministers ran into trouble with authorities because they wrote "too much" encouragement to conscientious objectors in camp. This censoring limited what John could write home, so we don't know all he endured. But much has been learned from his letters and from family and friends who kept his story alive through the past generations.

Mr. Milton Good of Dalton, Ohio, works at the Behalt in the Mennonite Information Center in Berlin, Ohio. He supplied copies of John's original letters, photos, and written documents, which are kept at the center. Also in 1963, an essay entitled "John Witmer, WWI CO" was published in the Mennonite Historical Bulletin. The Witmer family graciously consented to the use of this essay in writing this story.

A special thank you to both the Witmer family and the Goods who critiqued this manuscript for accuracy and gave encouragement to write John's story in book form.

As you read of John's faithfulness in the midst of hostility, may you be encouraged to stand firm for Jesus Christ, and be able to say with Paul, "I have fought a good fight, I have finished my course, I have kept the faith: henceforth there is laid up for me a crown of righteousness, which the Lord the righteous judge, shall give me at that day: and not to me only, but unto all them also that love his appearing" (2 Timothy 4:7, 8).

Contents

CHAPTER 1

April 17, 1918

W AR DEPARTMENT. John's hand fell limply against the postcard lying on top of the mail he had just pulled from his father's post office box. WAR DEPARTMENT. The stark black wording on the return address shattered all hope of a miraculous deliverance. There was no question; he was being called into military duty. With sinking heart he turned the card over and read the words in bold print.

BE ALERT Keep in touch with your Local Board
Notify Local Board Immediately of change of address

Kindly be prepared to report for duty between the 3rd & 6th of Sept. Official notice will follow later.

LOCAL BOARD
for the
County of Mahoning
4th Floor Court House
YOUNGSTOWN, O.

Stumbling down the post office steps, John's thoughts flew to Nola, his sweetheart. *If only I could share this devastating news with her now!* he thought.

Trepidation gripped him, smothering him in a numbness that spread from his heart to the soles of his feet. With fumbling fingers he untied Black from the hitching post, forgetting to give his horse the usual "hello" rub between the eyes. The horse seemed to sense his master's distress for he nuzzled John's arm instead of whinnying a welcome. With uncanny animal instinct, Black knew something was wrong.

Methodically John backed his horse away from the post office hitching post. His mind whirled in agitation as he tried to think of a way to escape being thrust into the midst of the world's unrest.

A whole year and eleven days had elapsed since President Woodrow Wilson, on April 6, 1917, declared the U.S. was entering World War I. How was it possible that he, John Witmer, a farm boy from the small town of Columbiana, just three days shy of his 21st birthday, was being compelled to go to military training camp? He knew nothing about fighting! Why, he knew nothing about the world except farming, training horses, and attending church where God's Word was taught and lived. He rarely moved outside his community except to take the train sixty miles west to Dalton to visit Nola Horst. A fleeting smile tugged at the corners of his mouth at the pleasant thought of seeing Nola.

"Why, Lord?" his lips cried. "Why is this Your will? For what good is this government order, an order I can't conscientiously take any part in? I love our free country I live in, but, Lord, I love You more." His spirit groaned under the weight of this cross.

John's mind and heart became a battlefield as he strove to accept the bitter disappointment the postcard brought to his life. *Am I willing to give my life for Christ? Is God asking me to surrender my hopes and dreams for the future? What of my friendship with Nola? How dark and foreboding the future looks when I try to find the answers myself,* he thought, chiding himself for letting his faith waver.

"Lord, I will trust. I will be true to Your bidding. If I am called to give my life that someone else may inherit eternal life, I will do so. And, Father, by Your help I will never disobey Your clear commands to love instead of hate or kill." He gripped Black's reins as he uttered the words aloud. Black's ears picked up at his master's commanding voice and he broke into a gentle trot.

Yet, a chill gripped John that not even April's balmy sunshine could dispel. He felt his human frailty and shrank from the unknown. What lay ahead? Would there be other COs at camp? Or would he need to face hostility alone? Would he even be granted CO status when he was examined? Or would he be sent to prison?

Lord God, his spirit cried out once more, *fill me with Your strength to face the unknown. My flesh shrinks from what is to come and fills me with fear.*

Once more his horse sensed the tension on the reins and responded by increasing his speed. Black's steady trot down Columbiana's cobblestone street soothed John's inner turmoil and he pushed his thoughts aside to concentrate on the day's work waiting at home.

Yesterday's rain brought spring plowing to a temporary standstill, but tomorrow I will be back in the fields, he mused. He loved the smell of freshly-worked soil and relished the prospect of spending the coming days out in the field with his horses. His farmer eye scanned the surrounding fields, noting their readiness for spring planting. What would become of his eighty-acre farm? *How long would someone else need to farm it? Should he sell his livestock and horses, or keep them?* Wearily he forced the unwanted questions into the background. September was still five months away.

Two weeks of steady fieldwork kept him farmbound before rains allowed him to take a Saturday off to visit Nola.

I hope she received my letter in time, and that a visit suits! he thought as he boarded the Pennsylvania Railroad train. Trains offered the fastest and most efficient way to travel between his and Nola's homes, as both their churches' mode of travel was by horse and buggy.

Riding the train gave him time to reflect on the questions that kept surfacing ever since he had received his draft notice. With the busy spring workdays, he had continually pushed them into the background. But now the questions concerning his farming swirled in profusion through his mind, swamping him with doubts and fears until he realized the enemy of his soul was using the uncertainties to destroy his peace with God.

Unmindful of the passengers around him, he bowed his head in shame. The tempter had caught him so easily! His lips moved in silent prayer to God. *Forgive my faithless questions and doubt,* he entreated earnestly. *Strengthen my faith, O Lord. You know the future. I believe Your divine words that You will never leave me nor forsake me. Remind me to never lose sight of the promise of Your keeping. Remind me to keep my thoughts centered on Thee. Thank You for answering my plea and for restoring my faith and trust in Thee. I now commit my life and Nola's into Your*

Almighty hands.

When the train stopped at the Orrville station near Dalton, John exited with renewed strength and inner peace. He hadn't noticed the stares of his fellow passengers or their raised eyebrows. His soul was flooded with such peace that he felt transported to the gates of glory, and his heart was bursting with praise. Comforting words from a hymn the youth had sung in the last singing flowed through him. The words stayed with him as he caught a ride with a farmer to within a mile of Nola's home. The message from the song continued to inspire him as he walked along. Before the Horst farm came into view, the song's melody rang from his lips, his clear voice singing out in heartfelt conviction.

> Take my life, and let it be
> Consecrated, Lord, to Thee;
> Take my moments and my days;
> Let them flow in ceaseless praise.

After singing the precious words once, he sang the song through again. As he sang it the third time, Nola, who was hanging out wash, spied him turning into the lane and heard the words of the last stanza.

> Take myself and I will be,
> Ever, only, all for Thee.

Seeing John brought a glow to her face. God in His goodness had given her the love of a man who radiated Christ's love. Her heart beat faster to think of sharing life with him. Just this spring he had bought a farm—another step in God's leading! Leaving the clothes basket she hurried over to meet him.

John and Nola had begun dating seriously after John was baptized and taken in as a member of White Mennonite Church on June 3, 1917, where his father

Daniel Witmer was minister. Unknown to the young couple, they had the prayer support of many in the church family. John lived a studious, conscientious life. Many of the older, mature Christians believed God would one day call John to the ministry.

Nola Horst's mother had died three years earlier when Nola was nineteen, leaving her the responsibility of mothering five younger siblings. As she conscientiously filled this vacancy, she won a special place in the hearts of her congregation. Her life showed her commitment to the Lord Jesus, bearing the characteristics of a godly woman. Those acquainted with John and Nola believed God's blessing rested on them, and they took an active interest in their friendship.

"Hello, Nola. It's good to see you again," John said, smiling. Her open, wholesome face was framed by dark hair parted neatly down the middle. A petite person, she complimented John's own slight frame.

"I have something to show you," he said seriously, handing her the draft notice.

Nola read it and her spirit sank. *Not John! Would he really have to report?* Looking up at him she pushed her panic aside and smiled bravely. "I heard the song you were singing," she said, her voice faltering.

John could read the pain and love in her face, and he felt humbled to see her pure unselfish love.

She took a deep breath. "The words you were singing . . ." she whispered. "The words have added meaning now and are doubly precious. And, John," her voice grew stronger and her eyes shone with conviction, "if we give ourselves to Him, all will be well, for God is in control." Her words of faith increased John's own determination to be faithful at all costs.

The afternoon hours with the family flew swiftly. Five-year-old Elias dogged John, until Sam used his fourteen years of wisdom to engage his help in cleaning out the barn stalls.

"John did not come to see you!" he told his little brother in disgust.

"I know he doesn't care," Elias wailed. "He talked to me and told me how I could begin training Star to lead. You just want me to do your work! Papa didn't tell me to do your job!" his voice shrilled in frustration.

"What's the matter here?" a deep voice asked as big brother Earl arrived on the scene.

Sam shrugged. "Just trying to give John a break from a little burr," he replied.

"In that case," Earl said as he turned to Elias, "maybe I could enlist you to help Mary Ann and Della churn a freezer of ice cream for supper." He tousled the curly head. "Does that sound better than cleaning stalls?" he whispered. "I'm sure the girls will need a good strong arm before the ice cream gets hard."

Elias rubbed his eyes and gave Sam a triumphant smile. Earl was seventeen, and Elias would gladly listen to him. Besides, Papa had already told him to obey Nola and Earl, but he had never said Sam could boss him around!

Nola served the family's standard Saturday evening supper of hot corn bread and potato soup. The ice cream churners beamed happily when John spied dessert and remarked, "Ice cream! Um! How did you know home-made ice cream is my favorite?"

All the hard work of turning the handle was forgotten as John took a generous helping and turned to them. "I believe you three are the ones I need to thank. I can't remember ever having been responsible to mix up ice cream when I was eleven, Della, or helping to turn the handle when I was nine like you, Mary Ann. I even saw Elias hard at work cranking the handle." He gave each a smile.

"Thank you for the delicious supper," John complimented as he rose to help clear the table. Carrying a stack of dishes to the cupboard, he set them down and rolled up his shirtsleeves.

"John, you don't need to," Nola protested.

"Then may I? It will be my pleasure. I do want to," he said, taking the dishcloth and starting to wash. The younger children quickly vacated the kitchen, leaving John and Nola alone. Both welcomed the privacy to share what lay heavy on their hearts.

It was a good hour later when John glanced at the clock ticking away the minutes. "I'm afraid it is almost time for me to catch the eastbound train. Nola, I want you to know how much I enjoyed this afternoon and evening. Just being able to talk to you about my draft notice has been a tremendous help. I knew you would understand how I felt and all my misgivings. But let's pray before I go," he suggested as they walked outdoors.

In the early evening twilight, they knelt beside the garden bench and committed all to their heavenly Father. Good-byes and waves were exchanged as they parted, both strengthened in their resolve to accept the divine will of God.

CHAPTER 2

July 1, 1918

$\mathcal{F}$urrow lines creased John's forehead as he sat at the kitchen table with pen poised in his hand. Once more he read the signed card before him. He didn't personally know the Youngstown businessman, Mr. May, an acquaintance of his father's, but he felt compelled to answer his letter.

June 29, 1918,
Mr. John Witmer,

Dear Sir,
*   I noticed your name in the paper as having registered. I wish you success without any misfortune whatever. Please read Psalm 91. I believe in the power of God and that he is able to take care of man.*
*   If you like horse training, do not forget to*

mention that fact when you are asked what you can do. They need horsemen too.

I will be glad if you will let me hear from you when you have time to write to me.

Hoping peace will soon be established and men will be permitted to go to their respective homes to enjoy their friends and families association.

Best regards to Papa, Mama and the rest of the family your self included. Respectfully.

N. A. May

Mother, who sat at the opposite end of the table sorting the last of their previous year's dried beans, noted her son's eyebrows knit in concentration. Her heart yearned for her firstborn.

How gladly I would change places with him! she thought. *If only he could have gotten a farm deferment!*

But no, God had chosen their son to fill another role. Her mother love sent a prayer heavenward. *I need Your grace, Lord, to encourage, to be strong, to unreservedly give my son into Your care and keeping. And now, Lord,* she communed with her Father, *give him wisdom of words as he answers Mr. May's card. That his writing would be a means of bringing spiritual awakening and conviction for truth in Mr. May's heart.*

She saw John bend over his paper and begin writing. *Thank You, Father, for answering,* was her thought of praise as she rose from the table with the finished beans.

Columbiana, OH, July 1, 1918
Dear Friend, Greetings!

I received your card today. Thanks for the word of comfort.

As we see the dark clouds gather before us and read of the awful distress of the nations of the world we are made to believe the nations have reached the condition mentioned in Ps. 9:17

But by reading Matt. 8:1 we are made to believe there is yet a traveler here and there.

After reading your card I believe you fail to understand that because I am a servant in Christ's Kingdom, I cannot fight. John 18:36

Therefore being commanded to let my light shine, Matt. 5:16, I shall endeavor to explain what we believe.

Taking Christ's sermon of the Mount, we have many of the commandments charged which we must not break. Matt. 5:19 Let us notice Matt. 6:15. We believe that Christ not only taught nonresistance but also practiced it. Read Matthew, Chapters 26 and 27.

The Apostles also taught that the weapons of our warfare are not carnal, but mighty through God to the pulling down of strong holds. II Cor. 10:4, which we believe they also practiced. They were martyred in very shameful ways. Nowhere do I find that they fought in self-defense or in defense of their brethren. Considering the above grounds we can easily see if it is wrong to fight it is wrong to help

fight. It would be against my conscience to
train horses for the army,

These are only a few of the many teachings
and commands of our Lord and Master which
we as Mennonites hold dear. If you desire any
more light of what we believe be free to ask.

May God bless us so when Jesus shall come in
His glory we might be found among those on
His right hand, to meet the Lord in the air:
and so shall we ever be with the Lord. Matt.
25:31-46 1 Thess. 4:17

Hoping to hear from you.

Sincerely Yours
John M. Witmer

*Bless the message of this letter, that Thy Word would
speak to Mr. May's soul,* John prayed as he folded his finished work. *I do appreciate his concern,* he mused. *To
think he took time from his work to write me personally!
That is humbling! I know Papa is respected in the community. For years he has been known as one of the few honest
horse traders in northeastern Ohio, with people coming
from miles around to buy his horses. I'm sure Mr. May felt
he was giving me helpful advice.*

*To be able to train horses? I love the work! I know I
inherited my love for horses from Papa. That would be my
first choice and working ground my second.* John rose from
the table with a light heart. The letter was answered.

"I need you to read this letter, Papa," John said, taking
it to his father who was studying at the far end of the
kitchen. "I'm sure May believed he gave me wise counsel,
but his counsel is worldly, not from God's Word. I will feel
better about my answer if you approve it."

"I'll be glad to, son," his father answered as he moved his Bible and reached for the letter.

CHAPTER 3

July 26, 1918

"*M*ama, I will be fine, I'm in God's hands," John consoled his mother as she wiped her tears with the corner of her apron. She stole another glance at the offending notice lying on the table. She couldn't stop weeping. She wanted to turn back the years of time, anything to postpone the dreaded day of her son's departure.

"Yes, son, I do know you are in God's hands. I do believe He will take care of you. It . . . it is just so final. So wrong. The world is full of hate, of wickedness, of evil. I'm sorry, it just caught me unprepared and . . . and . . . John, I do thank God you are His child."

She used her apron again, trying to stop the tears that persisted in falling. "Could you read your notice aloud?" she asked. "I can't seem to."

John picked up his final notice and scanned the contents.

Report for Duty

M. G. O. Form 65

Your Serial Number is   __296__   *Order No.*   __149__

Always refer to these numbers when writing.

BE ALERT <u>Keep in touch with your Local Board</u>
<u>Notify Local Board Immediately of change of address</u>

Kindly be prepared to report for duty the 6th of Sept.

LOCAL BOARD
for the
County of Mahoning
4th Floor Court House
YOUNGSTOWN, O.

"It says I need to report on the 6th. I have one more weekend at home, Mama," he stated quietly.

John took his final notice to his room to put beside the first one. Picking up the first draft, he reread the fine print to see if they had misunderstood anything.

Local Board for - County of Mahoning State of Ohio
NOTICE OF CLASSIFICATION
I II III IV V
A

John Witmer Order No. __149__ Serial No. __296__ has been classified by the District Board on original claim in the classes under which letters are placed on the above schedule, and on the grounds indicated by such letters (see Form 1001- A for key to meaning of letters). This entitles him to a place in Class I and he has been so recorded on the Classification List of this Local Board. Appeals may be taken from classification by a Local Board within five days from the date of this notice, by any person who filed a claim with this Local Board. Appeals may be taken from classification by a District Board within five days from the date of this notice only in certain cases specified in section——-of Selective Regulations and when claimed by a person who filed a claim of classification with the District Board. To file an appeal it is only necessary to go to the office of the Local Board and write your claim of appeal in the place provided on the registrant's questionnaire.

<u>7, 25, 18</u>	<u>S. M. Thompson</u>
Date	Member of Local Board

No. Even when they went to the local board and appealed for a farm deferment in person, it had not helped.

"You are classified I-A, which is active military," the officer in charge had explained. "The only thing you can do is report for duty when called, and we will put your request to the Board of Inquiry of Conscientious Objectors. It may be weeks until you are brought before the board, but there is a good possibility you will be sent to work on a farm. But that won't happen until after you are in camp."

Those had been encouraging words, words of hope, that his time at military camp might not be too long.

Since I heard from the Board what to expect, I'm not as apprehensive about leaving. Several weeks in military camp should be bearable! he consoled himself. *And if it isn't pleasant, I do have an ending to look forward to.*

He kept fortifying himself with those promises, but as the days crept nearer, he felt a sobering heaviness that he could not shake. Many times he felt driven to his knees in prayer, entreating his heavenly Father for strength and calm in the days left at home with his family.

I must not make it harder for my loved ones, he

resolved. *Through Christ I can do all things.*

God did answer John's petitions, for his family marveled at his joyful expression and calm acceptance, and they in turn were strengthened by his testimony.

John's draft notice affected the whole family. Enos, his younger brother, would turn twenty the end of September. When would he be called to serve? Seventeen-year-old Ezra came next in line. John's harvest would fall on his brothers' shoulders. Ida lagged a year and a half behind Ezra.

"I solemnly promise to write to you often," she informed her beloved brother in a tremulous voice. He knew she was on the verge of tears.

"Thanks, sis. I'll expect those letters," he answered, his voice unsteady. Precious memories were nearly overwhelming him.

Ida fled to her room upstairs to have a good cry. Oh! How she would miss John! None of her other brothers could ever fill his place. Who else in the family shared her love of reading and discussing books, answered her questions, and gave her enlightenment she sought? John was the only brother who helped her with dishes when he had time to spare. Why did there ever have to be a war! She could hardly bear to think of her dear brother in a military camp.

"Poor Nola. How can you stand it?" she whispered out the window to the trees, which seemed to sigh in agreement.

Two more siblings made up the Witmer family—thirteen-year-old Owen, and Mary, who was seven. They, too, hated to think of John leaving home.

Later, at the dinner table, John caught his family's attention. "Listen to what my friend Phares from Wakarusa,

Indiana, writes," he said, and then read from the letter.

> *I was to Goshen this morning to see the boys
> leave for camp. Sixty-three boys are going to
> Camp Taylor, Kentucky. All of them were farm-
> ers. Twenty-five are conscientious objectors of
> whom my brother Noah was one. It sure was
> hard to see him be taken away from us like
> that, but hope that the Almighty will always
> guide and direct him in all things. God has
> promised never to forsake us and we surely can
> rely upon his promise.*
>
> *Will Ramer is also with the group, and it
> must be hard for him. He was married a year
> ago.*

Each family member sat lost in thought as they contemplated how very soon they would be facing the same situ-
ation. John read further:

> *A neighbor widow got a message on July 9th
> that her son was severally wounded in France.
> He was one of the first boys drafted.*

"His poor mother," Anna Witmer said as she gazed lovingly at her family. "We have a hope and peace through
Jesus Christ. We know John will go into camp with Jesus
beside him. That boy's mother may not know Christ and
be experiencing only hopelessness."

"Each of us has a responsibility," Father admonished.
"Prayer. We live in uncertain times. Our boys need our
prayers for faithfulness, and the boys fighting in the war
need our prayers that they be given a chance to know Jesus

as their Saviour before they face death. And let us remember to pray for the peace of Jerusalem, peace within our hearts, and peace within our nations."

"Did Cousin Albert ever get his draft notice?" Enos asked. "Hearing from Phares reminded me of Albert's letter last summer. His number was way up in the 900s."

"That's right," John agreed, "only the first 600 were examined, and Albert hoped they wouldn't go any higher."

"I wish you had a 900 number," Mary injected wistfully.

"So do I." John reached over and tweaked her braid, causing Mary's somberness to dissolve into dimples. *So like Nola's smile,* he thought. *A deep dimple on the left!* He would miss Nola and his family! There was no doubt about that!

John's mind jerked back to the present when he heard his father say, "It may well be that Cousin Albert is never examined. If Wayne County needed only 170 for that call, it is possible the 900 numbers will never be needed. We hope he doesn't need to go, but we must remember that God says, "For my thoughts are not your thoughts, neither are your ways my ways.""

August passed in a blur. September arrived, and the Daniel Witmer family treasured each minute of this last Sunday they would be together as a family. On Saturday the women had worked doubly hard to prepare John's favorite meal. On Sunday when the Witmer buggies left the farm lane for church, a fat roasting hen was beginning to sizzle in the oven. Potatoes simmered on the back of the stove. Husked sweet corn sat under a clean towel on the sideboard waiting until dinnertime, to be plunged into boiling water just long enough for the tender yellow ears to be cooked to perfection. Ida's apple pies waited on the pantry shelf. She had baked them herself, a final gift for John. Their golden crimped crusts were a labor of love.

How gladly I would do the work over again if only John could be here next Sunday! Ida thought pensively. Then she pushed aside the unpleasantness of his leaving. *Today John is here. After church Nola will come. I will do my best to make this last Sunday a special day for him.*

A light haze hung low over the gentle rolling countryside. It looked as though another hot, muggy day was in store. Silage filling was well under way, leaving fields stripped of their corn. The last hay cutting was also in progress. All that was familiar imprinted itself on John's mind as he drove the mile and a half to where Nola had spent the night with a friend. He was taking her to church.

Having her along at last night's youth singing had been special, and now she would be with his family today. How glad he was that her father had consented to her spending the weekend in his community! In five days he would leave for camp.

Monday morning John hitched Black to his buggy. He was preparing to take Nola to the train station and accompany her home. The weekend had been a real encouragement. The words of encouragement, the promises of prayer, and letters from his church family continued to burn in his heart as he helped Nola climb into the buggy.

"I've been looking forward to this time when we can talk undisturbed!" John said, smiling down at her.

"So have I," she replied. A rosy flush spread beneath her dark lashes. "Ida is becoming quite an accomplished cook! I did enjoy sharing yesterday with your family and being at your church. Doesn't it remind us what a blessed privilege we have in being a part of a Bible-believing church?"

"My thoughts exactly! You must be able to read my mind! Ever since yesterday I've wanted to share with you how close to heaven I've been drawn. God is very real. It is as if the brotherhood has entreated God to impart special blessings on my life, and God has answered them far above anything I could ask or think. Nola, it awes me. I feel God walking beside me. The assurance of His presence has never been so vivid. I long to serve Him more fully. If you loved ones here at home were gone, nothing would tempt me to stay on earth. I feel all of heaven's angels are surrounding me."

John's communion with the Father brought Nola a deep joy that helped dim the sorrow of their parting. Truly, she and John had nothing to fear when the God of heaven and earth walked with them.

Before John returned home, Nola's father, Frank, added his blessing to those John had already received. "Though God saw best to take my wife and the mother of my children home to Him, I can still testify that through all my sorrow God has never forsaken me. His abiding love has only deepened. Testing either draws us closer or drives us farther away from God. His grace is always sufficient. God go with you and bless you, and may He allow you to return safely home."

"I have a little something for you," Nola said, slipping a small packet into John's hand. "Open it later. It is something I hope you can take with you."

Then it was time for John to leave. Sadly, Nola stood on the porch waving until John disappeared from sight. How long would it be until they met again?

"Every time I think of you, John, I will pray for you," she murmured her promise to the empty road that had taken her John away.

That evening in the privacy of his room, John opened his gift. Reverently he held the intricately stitched bookmark made from burlap. A dove rested above words formed from tiny embroidered x's, which read as follows:

The Lord make his face shine upon thee,

and be gracious unto thee:

The Lord lift up his countenance

upon thee

and give thee peace.

Nola! Nola! How much I love you, his heart whispered. Her gift was a treasure he would take with him to remind him of another sweet treasure awaiting his return.

CHAPTER 4

September 6, 1918

*Y*oungstown Courthouse teemed with people. The families, friends, townspeople, and military personnel mingled with the draftees heading for military training at Camp Sherman, Chillicothe, Ohio, making sure they received a proud send-off. Everyone wanted "their boys" to know they were heroes! To defend one's country was the highest sacrifice!

"Duty! Honor! Recognition!" the rallying cry rolled over the crowd.

"God bless you. Here is a Bible to take with you."

"Did you get a Bible, comrade? We want you to have this little Bible as you go to arms." Several Gideon International associates walked quietly among the men passing out New Testaments.

"Why, thank you!" John said, accepting the Testament and slipping the unexpected treasure into his shirt pocket.

"How thoughtful!" Mother expressed her appreciation

at the parting gift.

John nodded in agreement. The Bible against his breast assured him of his Lord's unfailing presence.

Boisterous laughter, whistling, shouting, exaggerated singing and hilarity surged around the Witmer family. "We can identify with the fathers of faith in Hebrews 11, who confessed they were strangers and pilgrims on the earth," Father said, voicing the family's sentiment. Those words took on a deeper meaning for them among the sea of celebrating humanity marching to the B & O train station. No further words were said, but each sensed the bonds of love, support, and grief of parting.

On entering the train station walkway, the mood of the crowd changed as weeping girls threw themselves into the arms of their young men. Laughter turned to tears as mothers embraced their sons. Fathers stood stoically, bracing themselves against outward displays of emotion but suffering inner turmoil. Would this be the last time their boys left home walking straight and tall in manly strength? When would they be sent overseas to face enemy lines? Would they return home? Would they be crippled and scarred, or would they return in a coffin? Some cursed the Germans for bringing the U.S. into the war. Heroism came with an awful price. An uncertain future loomed foremost in loved ones' minds.

To restore order to the chaos confronting them, officers barked instructions through bullhorns. A band drummed out the lively tunes of "Dixie" and "The Battle Hymn of the Republic," to brighten the sadness of parting.

"Recruits, form a double line!"

"Only enlisted men on the train walkway!"

"Begin boarding!"

"God go with you, son," were his father's last words as

he clasped John close. His mother's tender embrace and kiss, mingled with her tears, tore his heart as John left his family to take his place in line.

"May I have the privilege?" The voice and a hand on his shoulder startled John. He turned and looked into the face of Harvey Blosser, an acquaintance by name only, but a brother in the faith from the Brethren Church.

"Harvey!" Relief and gratefulness at having another of "like conviction" to share camp with him overwhelmed John. *Praise God! How good He is!* he thought, as he searched for his parents and waved. Gladly he saw them visiting with Harvey's family. Smiles of relief shone on the faces of the two Christian families. Good-bye was easier now. John and Harvey would both have companionship in a hostile environment.

When the hands of the big depot clock struck 8:30, the train whistle blew and the 12-coach train started moving out. Once again the crowd's temperament changed. Wild cheering erupted as people waved and shouted good-byes above the noise of the train's whistle blasts and the thundering beat of the band.

Boys on the train hung out the open windows returning the waves amid giddy cheering, shouting, and outlandish antics.

John and Harvey were glad they had chosen a seat towards the back of the train coach instead of being thrust into the middle of the coach's hubbub. Since both boys came from farming country, the passing landscape helped occupy the time. Conversation proved difficult in the surrounding noise as the other boys kept each other's excitement high by waving and shouting to every girl they passed, whether in a town or in the country.

"Warren County has level land, but the soil surely has

poor quality," John cupped his hand around his mouth as he spoke close to Harvey's ear.

"Must raise mostly hogs," Harvey replied and shrugged his shoulders at any attempt to converse.

At 1:00 their train pulled into Greenwich station and came to a standstill on a siding. "We are going to switch to the Big Four RR," someone hollered the news from the front of the train.

"Did everyone hear that?" another voice called out. "Now all together; we are going to switch to the Big Four RR!" A deafening roar enveloped the coach when most of the boys complied with their newly self-appointed leader. The noise stopped completely when several middle-aged ladies boarded the train with baskets of fruit.

"Take your choice of fruit, boys," one called cheerily, stepping down the aisle. "We represent the Ladies Aid of Greenwich and want you to know you are heroes to us. We thought you might be in need of refreshments. It's our way of giving you our heartfelt thanks. Help yourselves to grapes, plums, apples, or peaches." The men responded with cheers and clapping as the baskets made their way among them.

"Thanks!" Every young man on the train found his manners, which had been discarded since leaving Youngstown.

Harvey chose a peach, and John took a deep red plum. Um! It was firm and sweet. "It feels like breakfast vanished hours ago!" John murmured as he relished each tasty bite.

Soon after switching tracks, the train headed for Columbus, and box lunches were given to each. Things quieted down as the boys settled down to eat.

John and Harvey looked at each other before bowing their heads in prayer for the lunch. John tensed when he heard snickers from their seatmates. His prayer became a plea for grace. *Lord, we need Thy presence. Keep us under the shadow of Thy wing.*

Snickering turned to outright laughter.

"Preacher boys! We got preacher boys here!" several mocked. "Come on, pray out loud! We want to hear what preacher boys say."

"Want to fight?" the loud voice of their self-appointed coach leader snarled as he made his way towards the back of the train. John didn't look up. He was sitting on the aisle seat. His mouth turned dry and his stomach rolled, all hunger fleeing.

"We don't need your kind," the cold voice continued. "I know his kind!" his voice rose.

John shuddered as foul language spewed from his antagonist's mouth. "They need to be sent to the front lines. Yellow! They're filled with yellow! Send them to the front line. Get rid of them!" he sneered, contempt dripping from each word.

John lifted his eyes to meet those of the speaker. Compassion gripped him when he saw the hate mirrored before him. With their eyes locked, John prayed silently, *Almighty God, who sees and knows all things, touch this man's heart, soften him, and let Thy Spirit draw him, that he would think on You and realize You long for his soul. Help him see Christ's love shining from Harvey and me. Give us Your power to be a testimony for Jesus Christ while we are in camp. Lord, I need Your wisdom. Fill my heart with love, agape love.*

While John prayed, the young man spun around on his heel and returned to his seat.

"Did you see how I had them both cringing with just a look?" he boasted as several of his comrades slapped him on the back.

It was late afternoon when YMCA volunteers walked through the coaches passing out literature about Camp Sherman. "This might prove a good diversion," Harvey commented after accepting his pamphlet.

"Hopefully it contains useful information too. We know nothing of where we are going," John reminded him.

"True. All I know is that it is a new camp constructed for training when the U.S. entered the war, and that it serves Ohio, West Virginia, and western Pennsylvania."

"You forgot we know its location is Chillicothe!" John teased. "Or that Camp Sherman has a CO camp for boys. Any receiving CO status from Camp Taylor in Kentucky also are transferred there," he added.

"You are knowledgeable! I wasn't aware it had such a large CO camp," Harvey answered. "That is something we can look forward to, when we do move to CO camp."

Camp Sherman is located in the Scioto Valley just northeast of Chillicothe on Mound City, a burial place for the Hopewell Indians some 2000 years ago, John read the facts. *It trains 3600 men for each regiment with approximately 40,000 doughboys. It has a total of 2000 buildings.*

"Did you read this?" John pointed to the words. "It's astounding! They even have their own railroad systems to move supplies across the camp to the Hospital Group on the west side. This consists of 50 buildings interconnected by covered walkways. Wells provide twenty million gallons of pure water a day! I'm dumbfounded!"

"Makes a person feel like he came straight from the barn!" Harvey said, chuckling.

" 'Barracks are two-story wooden buildings,' " they read. " 'In order to feed and train 12,000 horses and mules a grain elevator was built.' "

"I remember my cousin Albert writing that the army

was buying horses in their area. But 12,000 horses!" John exclaimed.

"See here," Harvey scanned ahead. "They have dairy cattle barns and a milk-processing facility to supply fresh milk. A farm is cultivated by 100 German prisoners and by the conscientious objectors."

"That sounds interesting," John mused. "I would enjoy the chance to work alongside a German and talk with him."

"Maybe we will be moved real soon." Harvey's voice grew wistful. "I'm sure the opposition we've already tasted is very mild."

Both grew silent at the unpleasant memory, and then continued reading.

Camp Sherman includes a Recreation Hall, three theatres, the D.A.R. Lodge, along with three Knights of Columbus Halls, a Library, eleven Salvation Army Cabins, a Presbyterian Church, a Lutheran Church, a Jewish Welfare Center, and an Episcopal Church which gives draftees the latest opportunities.

Construction began June 28, 1917, with the first draftees arriving September 7, 1917. Construction is still going on, with October 1918 being the deadline for completion. A. Bentley and Sons of Toledo have averaged a building every 20 minutes.

"Every 20 minutes! How can that be!" John exclaimed. "The cost is estimated at four million dollars with one fourth going to the Hospital Group. Here is something else my friend Phares wrote about," John continued. "It says the 83rd division moved out and landed on foreign soil June 19. Phares wrote of a neighbor who was one of the first drafted, and he was severely wounded in France."

"Listen to this," Harvey took up reading. "'One rifle range is a 90-target, 1000-yard range.'"

"I think I will be choosy about what I write the folks back home," John decided. "I don't want them to worry needlessly. But they will enjoy hearing what camp consists of. It says Main Street of Camp Sherman is two miles long! Imagine! The immense layout boggles my simple mind."

By now John was weary of traveling. His head throbbed from the continual noise surrounding them. The unaccustomed talking, singing, arguing, and joking created constant bedlam that wore him down. He longed for the quietness of the barn where the only sounds were the munching of horses eating, the gentle swishing of their tails, or an occasional whinny to break the silence. He wanted to join his family at the supper table, be able to pray undisturbed, and share in meaningful conversation.

Darkness shrouded the outdoors while bright lights glared overhead. He closed his eyes to shut out his surroundings and recited Scripture to himself to strengthen his inner peace. Though he craved it desperately, there was no outer peace.

It was 10:00 o'clock when they arrived at camp and were taken to the barracks. When barrack numbers were given out, Harvey and John were separated.

"Pick an empty bunk and go immediately to the mess hall for supper." The officer in charge didn't waste any unnecessary words. John took the first empty bunk he found. Throwing his belongings up onto the top bunk, he left with his roommates to find supper. He was famished and didn't want to run the risk of getting lost.

That night he penned a letter home, closing with . . .

September 6, 1918

. . . every boy washes his own dishes. Do not worry about me but pray for me.
Sincerely Yours
John M. Witmer
25th Co 7th Tr Br
Camp Sherman OH.
P.S. Do not forget to put your address on the envelope that you send.

When he finished his note home, he opened his New Testament and read John 14 for comfort. Placing Nola's parting gift between the pages, he pulled up his one thin blanket, completely exhausted.

Back home at the Witmer farm, Father sat alone at the table where soft lamplight cast an inviting glow over a sheet of paper lying before him. Picking up a pen he wrote:

Dear Son,
Greetings in Jesus Name. I will write a few lines so I can have a reply to mail when we get your address.

He paused after writing the greeting. John's absence weighed heavily on him and Anna. He recalled their help-less feelings when John was rejected for a farm deferment.

"You have two other sons old enough to help," the offi-cer had snapped sharply.

Mama and I are grateful that God sent another Christian for you to be with. Today

after we got home I began training the colts in the west pen. Two are exceptionally good. That is about all I got done today. Our thoughts and prayers are continually with you.
May God bless us all from
Your Loving Father
D.C.W.

CHAPTER 5

September 7, 1918

*T*he bugle's first call shattered dawn's stillness as the first hint of light tinged the horizon. *Awake! Arise!* The notes called the sleeping camp. Moments later a voice barked, "Put on your uniforms. Be dressed and standing at attention outside the building by next call."

Fear seized John. He felt rising within him an icy numbness colder than the water in which he had washed his face or the chill floor on which he stood. "I can not, I will not, wear the uniform," he repeated his resolve in an effort to still his inner trepidation. He had no desire to look around at his fifty fellow roommates. All of yesterday's gaiety was gone. Each draftee hurried to obey orders, intent on being outside and standing at attention before the call sounded.

Father in heaven! his soul cried out in helpless anguish as he rested his weary head against the bunk for a moment. *Be with me. Give me strength to face this day. I have none.*

Peace replaced the fear, and John sensed the presence of Almighty God with him. Quickly he donned his civilian clothes, knowing he was deliberately disobeying his first military order. His first allegiance was to God. With firm steps he joined the line of uniformed men outside. God was with him! What did it matter if those around him tried to browbeat him with dark looks of hate, snorts of disgust, or muttered threats? God was with him!

Looking around, he saw row after row of unpainted wooden barracks. Where the barracks ended, other buildings started, creating a vast sprawling layout. *No wonder I am intimidated!* he thought. *The largest town I've been to is Youngstown!*

Barracks at Camp Sherman

Morning mists off Scioto River hugged the ground as the rising sun struggled to dispel the nip of autumn pervading the air. The bugle's second call rolled over camp.

"You!" exploded the barracks officer. "Get your military uniform on!"

A calm settled over John as he looked squarely into the officer's grim face. "Sir," he answered respectfully, his voice strong and steady, "I cannot conscientiously wear the military uniform. I am a servant of Christ's kingdom, and He has commanded that we love our enemies, not fight or kill."

"Report to Administration, immediately!" his officer barked, than strode on to finish inspection. John remained stationary. Where was Administration?

"Get!" someone hissed. John left the line of draftees, stumbling as someone purposely tripped him with his boot. The next soldier gave John a swift kick in the shins.

Show me, Lord! I don't know where to go, he prayed as he walked past row upon row of men standing at attention. He felt the presence of an unseen Guide directing his steps. As he walked, his courage and confidence increased. God was with him. He had the divine promise of Hebrews 13:5, "He hath said, I will never leave thee, nor forsake thee."

To his left, railroad tracks ran in front of a wooden stockade fence. Just ahead another track and well-used street veered to the right. Zanesville St., the signpost indicated.

Guess I will turn here, he decided. Zanesville St. soon left the barracks behind and turned into a large open space. Men in formation were doing some kind of training in a strategic pattern.

Probably drilling, John surmised correctly as he watched group after group of men marching in formation. Suddenly, without breaking step, one group of men all turned their heads to the right in perfect unison. When the next group approached the same spot where several officers were standing, they did the same thing.

John walked on, and before the third group reached the

New recruits in training

officers, he heard the group leader bark out a command. "Eyes right!"

Immediately the soldiers' heads swiveled to the right. No one broke step in marching; left foot, right foot; all in unison, giving special recognition to the standing officers. John's emotions tightened as he observed the soldiers with their crisp, pressed uniforms and gleaming shoes. Each held his rifle butt in his left hand with the gun barrel over his left shoulder. The sight was impressive! How was he to go against the tide? Would he be swept under?

"This has to be Main Street," he decided before crossing the wide, brick roadway which led him to a cluster of buildings with a sign, "Administration Building and Officers' Quarters." That was his destination. Opening the door, John stepped inside, coming face to face with Harvey.

Relief washed over both their faces as they broke into smiles. No words were needed to express their thankfulness at once again being able to share whatever trial they faced. They did not know that the heavenly Father was strengthening their faith for severe testing ahead.

Muffled, angry voices sounded from behind the closed door. Suddenly it was flung open and four officers strode into the waiting room.

"This has to stop! We will not tolerate insubordinate behavior," one man thundered, his raging face thrust close to theirs. "We are a country at war. You will do what we say! The place for you is right on the front lines!"

Both boys cringed inwardly, but showed no outward sign of cowering at the vile language filling the room. Both began praying as the verbal abuse washed over them.

"Sir," John spoke up when the tirade stopped, "for us to disobey God is wrong. The Bible says, 'We ought to obey God rather than men.' I can have no part in the military and that includes wearing the uniform."

"You will wear our uniform!" the angry officer spat. "Forcefully remove their civilian clothes if they refuse; then confiscate all their personal belongings," he snapped to the other officers beside him.

With sinking hearts they realized they would have to wear the uniform or be without any clothing whatsoever. God did not intervene for them when the officers grabbed them and proceeded to strip them of their clothing. In seconds, they were left standing alone, undressed, friendless, and forsaken. With hearts too heavy to talk, they silently put on the military uniforms and returned to their barracks where they found all their personal possessions gone, including their wallets with money.

My New Testament! Lord, I do rejoice to find they left me Your Word. John's heart overflowed in praise as he discovered it and his writing paper with his blanket. Opening the Testament, he reread the precious assurance recorded on the marker from Nola,

> The Lord make his face to shine upon thee,
> and be gracious unto thee:
> The Lord lift up his countenance
> upon thee
> and give thee peace.

The first day in camp seemed to have no ending. Respite from mocking, verbal abuse, sneers of contempt and harassment came only when mandatory curfew went into effect a half hour before lights were turned out.

I never realized how much the world hates Jesus. It is a hatred I have never before witnessed or thought people capable of possessing. How sheltered my life has been! John mused. *I was totally unprepared for what I experienced today. But I can't write home tonight what I've been experiencing. Physically I am fine. That is all they need to know.* With that decision he scribbled a few lines under the greeting.

> *I am getting enough to eat so far. Last night it was a little chilly out and feels like tonight will be the same.*
> *I hear we are to be examined on Monday. I am in my usual health. The treatment we get is not always what one would desire, but we are "looking for a city which hath foundations whose builder and maker is God" Heb. 11:10.*
> *May God bless us all.*

Now I'll write Nola a letter explaining camp. She will enjoy hearing all about its vast layout, John thought. A smile played across his face as the minutes ticked steadily by. Camp no longer held him captive. He was transported back home with thoughts of his loved one. Just before lights out he closed his letter.

It is an added blessing to have one Christian friend in the midst of thousands of enemies. The future looks very dark, but knowing I have the prayers of loved ones gives me fortitude. Thank you, Nola, for your prayers. I have already felt the effects of prayer on my behalf.

CHAPTER 6

September 10, 1918

My letter will be brief as the captain for our division told us we were not allowed to write much home.

Harvey and I now sleep in a big room by ourselves.

We never know one minute what will happen next but we slept good last night.

John stopped writing as his thoughts reverted to Sunday when he and Harvey had refused to take part in drill practice. One glance at Harvey's bald head glistening under the ceiling light sent his hand to touch his own shaven head. The awful experience flashed clearly before him.

Upon walking back to their room after Sunday dinner, they both had heard low voices talking from behind.

"It's them!" one hissed.

"Are you sure?"

Trouble! was all John had time to think before they were accosted from behind.

"Your names. Give us your names!" the angry voice of the self-appointed train car leader demanded.

"We'll teach you low-down cads! Think you can hide a traitor inside a uniform? Never!"

Hands grabbed them, shoving them into an open door of one of the barracks.

"Kneel down!" spat out another soldier.

John caught a swift kick behind his knees, sending him staggering to the floor beside Harvey. He winced as a thin rope bit into his wrists, and his hands were roughly tied behind his back. Neither boy resisted. Instead, John found himself praying for the embittered men who loathed them because of Jesus Christ. He had the assurance Harvey was praying too, and that helped him bear the searing pain that ripped across his head when a straight razor peeled off skin and hair. Blood flowed, but the ruthless shavers didn't stop until the job was finished.

Would they ever forget? No, but by praying, God gave them enabling grace to endure the torture. John still flinched when he recalled what followed.

"Get out!" commanded his persecutor when their hands were slashed free. John started to stand when a powerful kick against his shoulder sent him crashing to the floor. "That will teach you, preacher kid," snarled his antagonist. "Think you can join church to save yourself? You . . ." John shook his head, pushing away the painful memory and ugly words. He didn't want to dwell on it. Instead he focused on his unfinished letter.

I slept pretty good last night. My left shoulder is a little sore. Remember us in your prayers so

we may hold fast the profession of our faith.
Heb. 10:23

As he folded the letter Harvey asked, "How did your questioning with the authorities go today?"

"I don't know, but I do know God was with me. They accused me of being baptized last summer for the sole reason of avoiding military service. It troubles me now that I waited so long to take that step. I needed to be sure; I felt so unworthy and unready to take the baptismal vows. I struggled with assurance for strength, to remain faithful in every detail of my Christian life. Now I realize it was Satan tempting me. Instead of resting in God's power and promises, I was trying to find strength my own way. God knows my heart, Harvey. I must leave the future with Him. The Commander kept returning to the Old Testament, then questioned me on church history. I told them I haven't studied much of church history. History tends to change. I would rather study about Jesus Christ and His teachings because they do not change and are the only way to salvation."

"I'm interested in knowing what verses you used," Harvey probed, as his comrade grew silent.

"I used Matthew, Chapter 5, verses 38 and 39, where it says, 'Ye have heard that it hath been said, An eye for an eye, and a tooth for a tooth: but I say unto you, That ye resist not evil: but whosoever shall smite thee on thy right cheek, turn to him the other also.' Then verses 43 and 44, 'Ye have heard that it hath been said, Thou shalt love thy neighbor, and hate thine enemy. But I say unto you, Love your enemies, bless them that curse you, do good to them that hate you, and pray for them which despitefully use you, and persecute you.' Also John 18:36 when Jesus says,

'My kingdom is not of this world.' Another was found in Matthew 26:52 where Jesus said, 'Put up again thy sword into his place: for all they that take the sword shall perish with the sword.'

"I'm glad we brought our Bibles along, aren't you?" John added.

Harvey nodded in agreement before stating, "They sure questioned you extensively. I never used my Bible. They waved it aside, asked when I was baptized, my standing with the church, and what work I did in civilian life. When I said I was baptized four years ago they dismissed me."

"I can see their point of view," John acknowledged. "War is officially declared on April 6. I turn 20 fourteen days later, and in two months I am baptized and taken in as a church member. No wonder it looks to them as though I had ulterior motives. I'll confess my heart plummeted to my boots this morning when we were 'court marshaled.' I didn't understand that was the term used for us who are on trial until we are examined by the Board of Inquiry on Conscientious Objectors. I thought it was a prison sentence!"

"How much have you heard of Fort Leavenworth Federal State Prison in Kansas?" Harvey asked.

"I've heard of several who did not pass examination and were sent there. I guess if you do not get CO status, that is where you are sent. Maybe I should be preparing myself," John replied slowly. "The Commander did not seem to feel I was genuine."

"I've heard the board's sentencing is not consistent and often has no reflection on an individual," Harvey responded. "I've heard they seem to pick and choose who goes where."

John has received worse harassment than I have thus far,

Harvey thought. *He could be right when he speculates it may be because he so recently joined church. The government knows everybody's past history! I'll certainly not tell John some of the earlier horrors COs have suffered while in prison.*

Harvey breathed a silent prayer for his friend. *Lord God of heaven and earth, spare John from going to prison,* he pleaded. *Not our will, but Thine, be done.*

Though John did not possess robust physical strength, Harvey was challenged many times by John's deep spiritual commitment.

Harvey recalled what had happened to the Hofer brothers in prison. Three Hutterite brethren and a brother-in-law suffered appalling conditions when sent to Alcatraz, a federal prison on the Isle of Alcatraz in the Bay of San Francisco. On the way to prison they were treated as if they were criminals, chained two by two by their hands and feet. They even slept that way at night. When they arrived at prison, their treatment worsened. They were thrown into dark, foul-smelling dirt cells, and they were each given only one-half glass of water every twenty-four hours for the first 4½ days. The second day and a half they were made to stand with hands chained to a high bar overhead so they could barely touch the floor with their feet.

Harvey gave an involuntary shudder at the horrible misery of these men. When they were removed from their cells five days later, they were covered with boils and insect bites, and their arms were so swollen that they were unable to put on their jackets. Then they were severely beaten.

In the winter they were moved to Fort Leavenworth. The drastic climate change heightened their suffering. During the transfer they were again treated as dangerous criminals, with six armed guards escorting them. When they arrived at nearly eleven o'clock that night, the guards marched them down the middle of the street, herding them like cattle. Using bayonets, they drove them with shouts and prodding. The men struggled to hurry but were hampered by the chains that joined their arms together. With one hand they carried their bag of possessions and under the other arm they tucked their Bible and a second pair of shoes. Bathed in sweat, they arrived at the prison and were instructed to remove their clothes and wait for prison clothes to be brought. For two hours they stood outdoors in the rough winter air until they were nearly frozen. Finally they received clothes. But at five o'clock in the morning they were again sent to stand outside.

Two brothers became sick and were sent to the hospital. The other two were placed in solitary prison cells and made to stand for nine hours a day with their hands stretched through the prison bars, chained together. For two weeks they endured this while receiving only bread and water. The surviving brother-in-law said, "Life at Fort Leavenworth was like living in a palace compared to Alcatraz."

Harvey thought of the one brother's dying testimony. Stretching out his hands he said, "Come, Lord Jesus; into Your hands I commend my spirit."

The suffering these brethren endured for the sake of following Jesus Christ increased Harvey's determination to be faithful at all cost.

Harvey gazed around the cheerless room he and John shared alone. Beds and a washstand were all the furnishings. But the Hofer brothers would probably have found its comforts beyond that of a palace!

"Here, have a peach, Harvey," John said, breaking the

silence. "I got them in a package today, and they won't keep long. Tonight I need every bit of home love I can get, and I assure you, these peaches were packed with love and prayers!"

Before retiring, they spent a blessed hour sharing together in Bible reading and prayer. "I now feel fortified with heavenly power!" John said as they turned in for the night. "Heavenly power is enabling me to stand firm as a soldier in Christ's army."

Long before rising call, the frosty outdoor temperatures penetrated the single board walls, driving out any warmth that clung to the sleeping forms. John awakened and moved restlessly. Hugging the mattress, he wrapped his thin blanket closer and buried his bald head beneath it. *My, but it is cold!* he thought. Harvey's even breathing told him his friend wasn't suffering from the cold. *Right now it would be wonderful to have Harvey's insulation!* John smiled into the darkness at the thought. A fitful sleep returned, filled with dreams of home and the wood stove, its crackling fire dancing out the door as he added stick after stick of seasoned hardwood. Nola smiled from the doorway of the kitchen where she and Ida carried platters of fried chicken and bowls heaped with mashed potatoes to the table. Enos pushed his chair back farther from the roaring stove. He unbuttoned his shirtsleeve cuffs and rolled them up. Taking a handkerchief, he wiped the sweat from his forehead. John added more wood. Why wasn't he getting any heat? Why was Ezra throwing open the window? Didn't he realize how cold the room was? And why did Mother look worried?

Cold pressed in, enveloping him. In his dream he saw Nola put her arm around Mother and both fall to their knees beside the couch. Shivering violently, John jerked awake. His dream returned vividly, and he curled into a tight ball, longing for a heavy blanket.

If I only had my wallet, I could buy a blanket from the camp store! he agonized. Knowing the futility of getting more sleep, he turned his thoughts to solving the problem with the cold. Should he write home asking his family to send him money? Or should he ask the officers if he could have his wallet back?

Guess I will wait a couple of days yet and see if they might return it, he decided as the morning bugle call rolled over camp.

Sunlight tinged the horizon, announcing a new day, gently pushing the darkness into retreat, ready to bathe the country with its light.

What looms on the horizon for Harvey and me? Ah! We are bathed in heavenly power! Fortified with Your power, Lord, we thank Thee for this assurance. John felt ready to face the new day. He was not alone!

CHAPTER 7

September 14, 1918

"Drill! Drill now!" thundered the drill officer, his eyes boring into John's. John and Harvey had refused to fall into drill formation with the other trainees standing at attention in even rows across the open drill field.

"I'm sorry, sir, but I cannot obey your order when it goes against God's orders," John answered respectfully. He did not flinch under the officer's menacing glare. Instead, he called on God. *O God, give me calmness and strength. I do not want to antagonize this officer again.* He had hoped today would be a repeat of yesterday. After having been given the order to drill, the officer in charge had ignored them, allowing them to stand off to the side during training exercises.

Color heightened the officer's cheekbones, and his cold, hostile eyes never left John.

Lord, show me love where there is hatred, John

continued praying. Suddenly the officer's fist lashed out. John's head exploded with searing pain, and he felt himself reeling backwards under the powerful blow. Harley caught him before he fell and helped him back to his feet.

"Both of you!" roared the officer. "Stand together. Face forward. This is military training camp! I will count to three. Unless you join the rest of the soldiers in drill, you will be . . ." he stopped. Deadly silence hung over the field as the formation of listening soldiers waited for the verdict to be given the two despised men standing alone.

"Shot!" shouted the officer.

The word cracked like a bullet. John felt weak. He dared not look at Harvey. His head spun dizzily from the blow he· had just received. *Shot!* The word sounded so final, but in this hostile camp he almost welcomed the end of suffering. Would it be only moments before he would be in glory? Glory! Oh, to see his blessed Saviour's face! Jesus, who suffered and died, that he, John Witmer, could see Him face to face!

Divine thoughts filled him with unspeakable joy. Great peace coursed through him and his face shone with heavenly glory as he anticipated the marvelous meeting. The officer watched in disbelief at John's expression.

Why, this young man is not afraid of death! To realize a man in the prime of youth would die for what he believed right shook him to the core of his hardened heart. *Why doesn't he plead for mercy and fear death like other men?* He, one of the toughest officers in Camp Sherman, had no power over this young man. This unnerved him, and he hated the feeling.

Suddenly, admiration replaced the hatred he had felt, yet he loathed himself for his softness and felt helpless in his conflicting emotions. He saw both boys obey his order

52

as they turned to face the enemy. He saw their shaven heads. He had endorsed the shave as readily as the ones who gave it. Now, instead of seeing weak cowards, he saw staunch courage. *If all soldiers were as true as these two, what a renowned army we would have!* the thought flashed through his mind before he could stop it.

"One!" he shouted, leveling his gun to cover his confused thoughts.

"Two!" the word split the air without John or Harvey making a move to join the ranks.

"Three!" he lowered his gun. Swinging around to face the soldiers in formation, he barked, "About face!"

Striding over to the two he spat, "Report to the Community Group! And . . . " he stopped to wet his lips, "and take your Bibles!" *It's all I can think of for them to do. Let the officers at Community come up with a humiliating punishment.* He was through! Turning on his heel he began calling drill steps.

"I thought our time was up," Harvey murmured as they left the drilling field.

"Yes," John replied. "In a way it is disappointing not to be in glory, but it is also inspiring to know God still wants us here on earth."

"He must have more for us to do here at camp," Harvey concluded, thankful to be alive.

The Community Group was the hub of the entire camp. It consisted of eleven buildings, which included the Y.M.C.A., the D.A.R. Lodge, and the Community House. When the boys arrived, an officer was waiting for them with two boxes. Standing the wooden boxes on end and placing them quite a distance apart he ordered mockingly, "Sit and read aloud from your beloved Bibles. Don't you dare take your eyes off your Bible for even one moment! I will be keeping guard."

Hundreds of soldiers milled around the buildings as John sat on the box with his feet dangling above the ground. Opening his Bible he began reading at the 18th verse of Matthew, Chapter 1.

"Louder, we can't hear!"

"Are you sure your God can hear?" voices sneered as they heaped ridicule on the readers.

"Slackers!"

"Yellow!" Taunts came from every side with some mimicking his tone of voice and the words he read.

John cringed as those around tried to outdo each other in the usage of vile language. One boisterous group kept hooting uproariously, "We are educating them to speak the Kaiser's funeral!" John knew the boys felt they were giving them the lowest insult possible, for Kaiser was the ruler of Germany, an enemy nation.

Though John and Harvey were too far apart to hear each other reading, John was certain Harvey was receiving the same treatment. John read chapter after chapter amid threats too awful to repeat. He tried to close his ears to the curses and evil words from the sinful men surrounding him. As he read, he concentrated on what God was saying, and the marvel of Christ's love pushed away the filth of ungodliness. *Let someone hear these words of truth. Let some soul be drawn to Jesus. Convict a seeking heart,* were snatches of prayer he sent heavenward as he read the Words of Life. Great love welled up in his heart for the unsaved souls in camp.

"Get up! Stand on your box and read!" the officer would suddenly command, delighting in changing orders. Then he would say, "Lay the box down and sit on it."

Both John and Harvey meekly complied, being careful

to fully obey, whether they were to read or stand a certain way, or to read without taking their eyes off the Bible. None of these commands conflicted with God's Word. For the next days they gladly followed them, fulfilling them to the best of their ability.

More than once John nearly lost his balance when the box was kicked or shoved around. Physical threats came close to being carried out, but at the last second were averted.

God is so good! How marvelous is His answer to our plea for strength! Not once in all the continuous days of reading have our voices given out! John's heart thrilled at the miracle.

When the ordeal ended, John wrote home.

I read all four gospels except the last three chapters of St. John. Of course not in one day. The soldiers soon tired of making sport and the language we heard by this time was not as bad as before. Wednesday we followed one officer over the camp carrying our bibles. We walked some miles, do not know how many. We certainly should continue to pray for peace and deliverance and thank God that we are yet permitted to enjoy religious freedom.

Mail delivery became the highlight of each day, and hardly a day passed without John receiving at least one or several letters. Today proved no different. But with only time to read one letter, the rest would have to wait until evening.

"Listen to this, Harvey," he read aloud from an unexpected letter bearing the return address of the CO camp at

Report for Duty

Camp Sherman. "It is from Noah Wenger of Indiana."

> Dear Bro. In Christ,
>
> I heard you came to camp and wrote to your brother Enos for your address. I'm located in the C.O. camp, was transferred here from Camp Taylor the 25th of August. I don't know yet if they passed us a sincere C.O. or not. If they don't I suppose I'll go to Fort Leavenworth in Kansas. Harvey Weaver, Will Ramer and Lewis Ramer are also here. They kept John Ramer at Camp Taylor as he is in guardhouse there.
>
> How are you being treated here? Can you get around in camp in the evening? If you can you might look us up at the C.O. camp. We can't get away at all. If you can't I wish you would write at once. Wishing you God's richest grace and blessing. I remain
>
> > Yours in Christ
> > Noah W. Wenger
> > 158th Depot Brigade
> > C.O. Camp
> > Camp Sherman

"Wouldn't that be wonderful if we could go see the boys?" John said longingly.

"Or better yet, join them," Harvey agreed.

After supper, John was called to Headquarters. *Now what?* he wondered to himself as he trudged wearily to the office. It had been a hard day with the constant walking, following the officer wherever he went. The waiting room held unpleasant memories of being forcefully undressed. *I left home just eleven days ago? My, it seems far longer than that!* he thought.

"John Witmer," an officer called.

John rose as his name was called and was ushered into the main office. Two officers stood behind the General. John recognized one as being in charge at his questioning several days before.

"John M. Witmer," the General looked him squarely in the face as he said his name.

"Yes, Sir," John replied.

"Upon reviewing your records, we responsible for Camp Sherman's administration have determined that you, number 296, Private John M. Witmer, order number 149, can be allowed to transfer to CO camp in the near future and wait for the Board of Inquiry on Conscientious Objectors to call for your examination."

"Thank you, Sir," John stammered, stunned to be receiving the coveted transfer.

He swallowed, and then continued, "I appreciate your consideration."

The General raised one eyebrow slightly. *Consideration? Doesn't this private realize it's the mistreatment he has been receiving that has qualified him, not consideration? Besides, with these boys gone there should be more peace at camp!*

"Private dismissed," he answered crisply. These CO boys were a strange lot.

A man has no secrets here, John thought as he returned to his barracks. *But I guess that is part of their work.*

Harvey was also notified that he would be allowed to transfer. Now all they needed was patience while waiting for the transferal date. John almost forgot his letters from home as he rejoiced in God's goodness. He would soon be surrounded with friends! He opened Ida's letter and concern replaced rejoicing as he read.

> *Dear Brother,*
> *It is quite rainy this morning. Enos just got back from registering.*

Would Enos need to suffer the same treatment he had been receiving? John let the letter fall as sadness wrapped his heart, squeezing out the happiness of his transferal. *Not Enos, Lord. How could I endure it if he faced this same opposition?* Anxiety plagued him as he opened his little brother's letter.

> *Dear Brother John,*
> *How are you getting along. Did you get those peaches. We sent you some. It was about a dozen.*
> *It rained yesterday. We cut some corn yester-day. It is too wet to sew wheat today and may be it is too all week. Mamma wonders If you get butter on your roasting ears.*
> > *From Your*
> > *loving Brother Owen*

Owen's letter cheered him, bringing a smile as he read the words Owen had so lovingly labored over. Father added a few lines, closing with encouragement.

> *May the good and Holy Spirit guide and direct us in ways which God would have us to go.*
> > *From your loving*
> > *Father*
> > *D.C.W.*

John put his letters away, and taking a sheet of paper he wrote home.

I guess you wondered why I did not write more, but some of the threats were so horrible that I am glad that you dear folks at home were not near enough here to see or hear what was going on. But we were not hurt. Praise His Name!

CHAPTER 8

September 16, 1918

*L*etters from home! He thought of them as precious sheets of paper giving him words of encouragement to remain faithful. They also reminded him of blessings he was missing.

When Enos wrote about Saturday night singings, it stirred in John an intense longing to again spend several hours singing hymns with other Christian youth. *A person doesn't realize how meaningful church is until it is taken from him,* he mused. While John contemplated the blessings waiting him at home, his family sat around the dinner table rejoicing over the good news his letter contained.

> *There are some officers here who use kind words when they talk to us, which we certainly appreciate. There is a soldier here from Laurence County who treats us very nice and most of the others do now, but they try hard to*

get us to give up our faith.
The inoculation and vaccinations which I
got last week did not make me sick at all. I
expect another one tomorrow.

"Thank You, Lord, thank You," Anna's heart throbbed with gratitude.

Unknown to the loved ones sharing his letter miles away, John was lost in a very personal letter. Reverently he tucked his sweetheart's letter under his Bible so that he could read its contents again. Nola's letters revealed the depth of her personal experience with Jesus Christ. With each letter he found his love deepening. How unworthy he felt! Yet he rejoiced that God had led them together. Her letters transported him above the hardships of camp, giving him additional fortitude to endure. A fragment of a verse from Psalms she had written in an earlier letter kept surfacing. When things got rough he found himself repeating the promise, "But joy cometh in the morning."

While Nola's thoughts often took flight to southern Ohio, wondering how John was making out at camp, home duties beckoned at every turn. The responsibility of caring for her motherless siblings often stretched her time to the limit. In rare moments of leisure, she worked at piecing a quilt for her hope chest. Lovingly she stitched together fabric strips beginning with light yellow, pink, and ivory, then to varying shades of greens, brown, and dark wine to create a patchwork pineapple quilt. Sewing kept her hands busy but freed her heart and mind. During these moments of quiet freedom, her heart communed with God, entreating mercy, strength, and wisdom for her beloved. Love and prayer flowed through every stitch she took. Home and camp seemed worlds apart with letters being the only source of contact between the two.

One day John received a letter from his cousin, Walter Witmer, of Indiana, describing the camp where he worked. The four CO boys at his camp would go out to a large hog farm and help the farmer with his work. *Maybe we can soon be doing things like that,* John thought wistfully as he returned from getting the mail.

"Go on for dinner," Harvey said as John poked his head in the door to see if his friend was ready to leave. "My shoelace broke and I want to finish mending it. Go ahead, I'll run and catch up," he insisted as John hesitated.

A couple of minutes later Harvey surveyed his patch job with satisfaction, tied his shoe, and hurried across the room to join John. Pausing at the door he waited for four soldiers to pass before he stepped out. He did not notice the four ahead of him exchanging furtive looks and whispering. The first thing he knew, they had turned around to face him.

"Thought we should join you," one drawled as two others grabbed his arms. The four pushed Harvey off the path and hauled him through a door into a nearby building.

"Thought you pulled a good one when Major General Glenn wouldn't shoot, didn't you?" another taunted. Harvey didn't answer.

"We aren't afraid to finish the job," the first speaker boasted.

Bump, bang, bump, up the stairs the foursome dragged him roughly. He gritted his teeth to keep from crying out in pain as his back jarred against the steps.

"Perfect!" one of them called from the open window, looking down at a cement slab below. "That will make a great landing place when we drop him!"

Harvey's attackers pushed him headfirst through the window, letting him dangle while they held onto his feet. Blood pounded in his ears, and the world went black as his head started spinning.

Through a fog he heard someone speak. "Count to four, and we will let him drop."

"Okay! One! Two! Three!" Then the counting stopped.

In the distance a voice blurted, "I'm afraid to count four."

Hope rose within Harvey. One of the men holding his feet quickly replied, "If you're afraid to count four, we're afraid to drop him." And back through the window he was pulled.

Thank You, God, for again intervening and sparing my life, Harvey breathed. Praise surged through him, numbing the pain searing his bruised body.

"Hey! We're going to be late for chow! Let's get out of here!" one soldier said loudly. He slapped Harvey soundly on the back, and the four hustled him back down the stairs and out the door into bright sunlight. Harvey stumbled along, his back and ribs protesting, but rejoicing that he was only bruised, not broken.

Camp seemed extra oppressive that night. Homesick for the sight of loved ones, John took up his pen.

I just asked an officer if it would be all right to have someone of the home folks to visit me. They said it would be all right so I hope some one or a few of you can come soon as the time gets pretty long. Sunday would be a good time for you to be here.

James 1:2 & 3 are precious words to me. (My brethren, count it all joy when ye fall into

September 16, 1918

divers temptations; knowing this, that the trying of your faith worketh patience.)

           May God bless us

           Sincerely

           John M. Witmer

CHAPTER 9

September 26-27, 1918

*C*old, bone-chilling dampness became John's nightly companion and left him in a numb stupor. With temperatures dipping into the low thirties, he slept fitfully, never able to get the rest he needed. Sleepless nights drained him of physical strength, bringing a struggle with discouragement.

Ever since Enos's visit on Sunday, homesickness dogged him. Talking with his brother had filled him with an infinite longing for normal home life. He couldn't shake the tiredness clinging to him. Tonight was no better as he shivered, huddled beneath his thin blanket on the hard, narrow bed. Even though he slept with his uniform on, it was not warm enough to ward off the cold. He had no extra clothing, for his confiscated belongings had never been returned. How he wished for the heavy shirts and winter jacket Mama had so lovingly packed for him.

"Harvey doesn't seem to mind the cold. Why do you

need to suffer so?" the tempter whispered, using the dismal dark of night to plant seeds of pity and doubt. "Haven't you endured more physical abuse than Harvey?" the thought persisted in the stillness. "Does God not care? Is He not showing favoritism? If God really loved you, He could give you warmth!"

John tossed and turned as the adversary of souls subtly wove his web of deceit. "You can't take another night like this; it is simply too hard."

John's heart and soul wrestled against the powers of darkness as Jacob of the Bible had wrestled the angel. Feeling utterly defeated and forsaken, John cried out to the God of heaven and earth for help.

Oh, Father, do not forsake me in this hour of trial. Give me power to withstand the enemy of my soul. It is almost more than I can bear. Without Your strength I am nothing. I feel like David when he wrote, "My God, my God, why hast thou forsaken me? Why art thou so far from helping me, and from the words of my roaring? O my God, I cry in the daytime . . . . Be not far from me; for trouble is near; for there is none to help."

God did not leave John destitute. He heard his cry and the enemy departed. John felt his spirit lifted as Jesus reached down and took the burden of cold, of self-pity, of discouragement, and loneliness.

"Forgive me, oh my Father," John repented as he realized he had forgotten to cast his cares upon the Lord. Instead he had been wallowing in self.

Calm replaced the inner turmoil, and though he was still physically cold and weak, he felt God's power within. He would rely on God's strength. By the grace of God he would not shame his Saviour's name, but remain true no matter what the cost.

John's heart sang with praise for God's forgiveness and enabling power. *Unto thee, O Lord, do I lift up my soul. O my God, I trust in thee: let me not be ashamed, let not mine enemies triumph over me.*

How does the verse go in Revelation? John cast around in his mind until he clearly remembered. *"And they overcame him by the blood of the Lamb, and by the word of their testimony; and they loved not their lives unto the death." By the blood of the Lamb! I, too, have access to the wonderful power in the blood.* His being thrilled at the blessed promise. Silently his heart sang the words of victory.

> Would you be free from your burden of sin?
> There's pow'r in the blood, pow'r in the blood;
> Would you o'er evil a victory win?
> There's wonderful pow'r in the blood.
> There is pow'r, pow'r, wonder-working pow'r
> In the blood of the Lamb;
> There is pow'r, pow'r, wonder-working power
> In the precious blood of the Lamb.

He was reminded that he, too, could say as Jacob did after wrestling with the angel, "For I have seen God face to face, and my life is preserved."

> Would you do service for Jesus your King?
> There's pow'r in the blood, pow'r in the blood;
> Would you live daily, His praises to sing?
> There's wonderful pow'r in the blood.

Yes, Lord, I will. With firm resolve he answered the song's searching questions. *I will do service for Thee. By Your power I will daily sing Your praises.*

Report for Duty

Right after breakfast John and Harvey went to get their third and final inoculation. "Hope these shots keep us from getting the flu," John remarked as they left the hospital compound. "The nurse did say cases are being reported, and they hope it doesn't become an epidemic."

The long walk to and from the Hospital Group left John totally exhausted. *Rest, rest.* His feet plodded one step at a time until he reached his room and lay down. But sleep eluded him.

Troubled thoughts dwelt on the uncertain future, which loomed darkly before him. *Lord, what are You trying to tell me? I need Thy wisdom. Show me what You want me to do,* he prayed. The financial obligations of his farm and livestock burdened him. Was it fair to leave his responsibilities to others?

Prayerfully he weighed his home responsibilities. *Is not life fleeting? And heaven's door only a shadow away? Are you prepared to forsake all and follow Me?* Loud and clear the unspoken questions confronted him as he sought answers for the future.

Yes! he answered in his heart, *and God's promises are just as sure! I feel strongly that God is asking me to leave my life completely in His hand, to sever all earthly obligations at this time. He has answered my petition. I may never have need for the things in this world.* The thought was sobering, but he marveled as a quiet rest filled him to overflowing. Taking up his pen and paper he wrote:

> *I am now ready to dispose of my farming implements and stock I do not know any more what will be in the future.*
> *Yesterday some said this company would be moved today but I did not hear anything*

today. I do not know when it will be.

As the morning progressed, his arm hurt more and more until he could barely use it. "Do you think I am having a reaction from the shot?" he asked Harvey. "Probably if I can sleep tonight, I'll be fine tomorrow," he answered his own question, too weary to talk. He rested but a short time, then woke with a pounding headache and chills that spasmodically gripped his body.

Harvey became alarmed when he checked on John, and he asked the barracks commander what he should do. "Appears as if he may have reacted to the shot," the officer said. "Just have him stay in bed and see if the fever passes by evening."

Early that afternoon, three young men entered John's room and stood in silence watching the sleeping occupant. After a few moments, the one closest to the bed cleared his throat and called, "John?"

John's eyes flew open. "Enos?" he whispered. "Enos! Is it really you? Or am I dreaming?"

"No, it's me, brother," Enos answered unsteadily. He was hardly able to force the words past the pain welling up inside him. John looked terrible! He was so pale, thin, and wasted, and deep lines were etched across his forehead.

Enos reached to clasp the thin hand stretched out to him. A gladness surged through him at seeing his brother again. John's face was wreathed with smiles, erasing the lines of pain and suffering as he beheld the familiar faces.

"Sam and Verton. It is so good to see you too," John said, reveling in the richness of his unexpected company.

"We have only a couple hours before we catch the bus home," Enos said, "but let's make the most of our time together."

Enos was determined they would be an inspiration to his brother. The next two hours flew by as they shared home news, got a glimpse of camp life, and strengthened each other by singing songs of faith and praise.

"Thank you doesn't even express my thanks for your coming," John said as he bid them good-bye. "But it is the best I can say. I can't begin to express the encouragement this visit has been. God bless you and keep you safe as you travel home."

After his visitors left, John reached for the day's mail. *Thank You, Lord, for the gift of family and friends,* his heart breathed in thanksgiving as he opened a letter from Uncle Jacob.

As he read, tears came to his eyes. John realized God had known he needed encouragement not only by mail, but also by flesh and blood visitors. Previous trials faded as John read again the written words, savoring each nugget of truth.

> *I am a poor hand at writing letters but I certainly hope you are receiving good treatment at present as well as at all times and that you are enjoying yourself as good as you can under conditions and rejoicing in the Lord. Will close for this time hoping you are assured that I always remember you.*
> *From your loving Uncle and brother*
> *Jacob*

". . . and rejoicing in the Lord." John reread the phrase. How many times he had forgotten to rejoice! *I must stamp those words firmly on my heart so that I won't be found guilty again,* he resolved. Opening Sister Ida's letter, he smiled as he noted her closing instructions to read the first three verses of Psalm 125.

Finding the reference, John read, "They that trust in the LORD shall be as mount Zion, which cannot be removed, but abideth for ever. As the mountains are round about Jerusalem, so the LORD is round about his people from henceforth even forever. For the rod of the wicked shall not rest upon the lot of the righteous; lest the righteous put forth their hands unto iniquity."

Thank you, dear sister, his heart whispered. God was so good! He had made it possible for Enos and friends to visit today. He knew loved ones and church brethren were praying for him, and daily they wrote to let him know of their love and concern for his well-being. How much more God must care about him.

Supper aroused his appetite for the first time in days. "I do feel better since eating," he said.

"That's good to hear!" responded Harvey. "Maybe you'd like to take a walk with me?"

"It has been a wonderful afternoon," John replied, "but I guess I'll head back to our room and leave you to enjoy a solitary walk! A book may be better company anyhow," he said with a laugh as Harvey pretended to retreat with injured feelings.

He had barely begun reading when Harvey burst into the room calling, "John! I have permission for us to walk over to the CO camp. Let's go right now!" he urged, his eyes alight at the unexpected privilege.

"Wonderful!" John exclaimed, thrusting his book aside. The thought of visiting with friends again invigorated him in soul and body. "There is no way now that I'll let you take a solitary walk tonight," he added with a laugh.

The CO camp was a good mile from their barracks, but

the distance was covered in a short time. John hardly felt his feet touch the ground, for his mind soared ahead to the reunion with fellow Christians. He knew Will Ramer was at the camp, and he felt a special kinship toward him. Will's father, Bishop Martin Ramer of Indiana, worked with the ministry in John's church, and the Indiana-Ohio churches had conference together twice a year. Will had been transferred to Camp Sherman the 26th of August.

The boys discovered the CO camp consisted of tents with dirt floors, each shared by four or five boys. Though the canvas walls offered minimal weather protection, John would gladly have traded his wooden barracks to stay here. A close spirit of brotherhood prevailed among the various Mennonite, Brethren, Amish, and German Baptist boys that made up the camp. The men were bound together by a common desire to serve the Lord Jesus and obey His Word.

Time took wing as they shared experiences, sang hymns, and prayed together, giving each other fresh courage. Too soon, the visitors reluctantly said good-bye and headed back to hostile quarters.

The stars glittered and a luminous, silvery, full moon rose over Camp Sherman. A stiff breeze blew off the river, wrapping the night with a chill blanket. The walk back seemed endless to John as he battled against the cold overtaking him and sapping his strength.

The next day a postcard arrived from Enos.

It is 8:30 and we are at the State Capital now. If we had known everything we could have waited on the other bus because the train was taken off the track

so we cannot get one for a few hours yet.
Wishing you God's richest blessings.
                    Your brother
                    Enos

As John read the postcard and remembered the treasured visit of the day before, the miles between dissolved, and he was warmly wrapped in the love of home.

CHAPTER 10

September 28, 1918

I've got to eat breakfast! If only my head didn't throb so every time I cough. John winced as another wave of pain washed over him. *I wonder if eating will help my fever? Wish I could remember what Ida says. Is it feed a fever, starve a cold, or starve a fever, feed a cold? But guess it hardly matters*, he thought dully as he forced himself to swallow a few bites of hot oatmeal.

By the time the others were finished eating, John was ready to return to the barracks.

"Just do as much of the routine morning cleaning as you can," the officer in charge advised kindly when he saw John's pale face.

Sweeping out the barracks drained his already weakened body, but before collapsing into bed, John rubbed his throat and chest with a decongestant salve Enos had brought from home. The liberal coating of salve and several hours of sleep relieved his congestion, but when dinnertime came, he stayed in bed, wrapped in his blanket.

This will be a good time to write a letter home, he decided as he reached for his pen and paper. Home! In the stillness of the barracks, beautiful thoughts of home tugged longingly at his heart. Then with sudden clarity, startling questions came to him: *Do I long for my heavenly home as much as I desire to return to my earthly one? Is God using this illness to speak to me? Do I have my priorities where they belong?*

Lord, John prayed, *You know my heart. Search me, O God, and know my heart: try me, and know my thoughts: And see if there be any wicked way in me, and lead me in the way everlasting. Forgive me for questioning Your divine will. I do yearn for heaven and the joy of seeing You face to face. Increase my faith, Lord, that I will not be found wanting when You call me home,* his heart cried in contrition. A great peace enveloped him as he began to write to his earthly loved ones.

> *I do not have my own clothes yet nor my pocketbook. Please send me a money order of eight dollars. I can buy a blanket at the store. I asked for my pocket book this morning and may get it today in which case I shall buy a blanket tonight. I also have a blank check (Enos left with me.) I do not know if they will accept it or not but I will try it.*

Weariness overtook him, and he laid down his pen. He was so tired! A shiver coursed through him, and he shook with chills. He drew the blanket closer, and in his weakened condition, he thought again of home. Dear Papa and

Mother. Enos, Ezra, Ida, Owen, and Mary. And dear Nola. Praise God, they were all praying for him!

Falling into a fitful sleep he dreamed of his earthly home. Vivid pictures portraying the cheery, peaceful atmosphere of home pervaded his dreams. Home! He could hear the quiet contented noises of the barn animals feeding. Ida's rich soprano floated in harmony with Mother's humming as they worked side by side in the kitchen.

Home! Tantalizing aromas of fresh baked bread and spicy apple pies swirled about him. Song sparrows sang in the maple trees, then scolded the barn cats when they tried to sneak into their territory to stalk them. The wood stove snapped and cracked as a burning log fell, settling farther into the red-hot coals. Nola's dark eyes sparkled, and she dimpled in a radiant smile. Black's harness jangled in his eagerness to reach town.

His dreams changed to heaven and he saw his heavenly home waiting for him, God's beloved child. He saw the city streets of pure, transparent gold as they gleamed and shone under the glory of God who sat on the throne. He saw the walls of jasper and beheld the dazzling light pervading the golden city. The crystal river sparkled in glittering brightness as it flowed out from the throne of God. It was too wonderful; he could not look at it. He turned away from the blinding light.

Rapid rifle shots burst through his dream and jerked him awake. Round after round from the practice rifle range pounded the targets, making camp sound like a battleground. The pulse of army activity enveloped him, trying to drown out his vivid dreams of heaven and home. Shouts and whistles and the constant moving of camp vehicles and personnel reminded him that he was caught in the giant whirlpool of Camp Sherman's perpetual motion without any way to escape.

It feels like three years instead of three weeks since I left home! I feel old and helpless, like I'm held captive in the grip of earth's bonds. O Father! Even so, come, Lord Jesus, his heart cried.

"A letter for you, John," Harvey said softly, as he approached the bed where his friend lay as still as death, his eyes closed. *How pale and thin John has gotten,* he thought with alarm.

Oh, John! Are you going to be all right? Why is it you have always received the harsher treatment? he thought, frustrated at his own helplessness. If only there were something he could do to relieve his brother who had less physical stamina for the hardships thrust their way. *You may be weaker physically,* Harvey contemplated in silent tribute, *but your spiritual steadfastness, your uncomplaining spirit, and your commitment to truth, give me constant inspiration. I praise God for your example.*

"Read it to me, Harvey. My eyes aren't focusing right," John whispered, disrupting Harvey's musings. "It is from my uncle," he explained.

> *We are a tribute of gratitude to God. He has yet spared our unprofitable lives and let us stand as miracles of grace on this side of the grave and eternity and it surely seems He must have a work for us to do yet. So let us meet our duty bravely casting all our care upon Him for he careth for us. God feeds the ravens, clothes the grass and cares for the sparrows and the lily He arrays in Majesty and none falls to the ground without the Heavenly Father's care. If He so cares for*

these how much more will He care for us.

"Harvey," John said quietly, "doesn't that make you feel so unworthy? God has done so much for me, and I so little for Him." John closed his eyes to rest, and Harvey left his friend with the question ringing in his ears and a renewed zeal in his heart.

John was left alone, thinking of God's goodness and protection. *God's protection surely has been over me,* John thought. Just yesterday he had had a miraculous escape with only a scratch from a deadly, razor-sharp bayonet.

It was the second time he had felt sure he would be hurled into eternity. What else had saved him but the hand of God upon his tormenters! He had thought taking a walk in the outdoor air would be just the tonic he needed, but instead, it had turned into a nightmare.

He recalled the paralyzing numbness which gripped him when two soldiers grabbed him, yelling, "Death to slackers!" and raced him towards a leering soldier holding, directly in line with John's head, a rifle with a bayonet.

At the last second, with a surge of divine strength, John had ducked his head, and the blade flashed by, its cold steel only grazing him.

That night John wrote a very brief, one-sentence note home. His hand persisted in trembling so that he had trouble controlling his pen enough to form letters.

Could you send me some agriculture magazines?

When his family received the note two days later, Anna Witmer read it in alarm.

"Why, Dan," she cried. "Look at his handwriting! It is hardly legible!"

"It looks like an old man's writing," Mary concluded with seven-year-old wisdom.

The next day the family received the letter John had posted the morning before he sent the one-sentence note.

I'm not feeling well today.

"What can we do?" Mother fretted. "I am worried he isn't getting the care he needs. It says in this letter he needs another blanket. Do you think he was able to get one? Oh, Papa, let's go to Columbiana and send a money order immediately!" Anguish tore her heart at the uncertainty of her son's sickness and her helplessness to do anything.

"Anna," Father gently called her name to calm her, "let us first pray and commit all to our heavenly Father. Though we do not know the circumstances, God does."

"I am so distraught, I can't think clearly," Mother admitted, wiping her tears.

John's family knelt together in prayer and humbly petitioned their heavenly Father for His mercy. Although praying replaced their agitation with peace, yet they carried a burden for their beloved son and brother.

"Ezra, you can ride your bicycle to town and mail a money order," Father decided. "But before you go, I want to write a letter to put with it."

After Mother brought paper and pen, Father sat at the table and wrote:

Was very glad to hear from you. Hope they will have mercy on you and give you your clothing and money before long. If you need anything more just ask for it and we will send you what you need.

You wrote that you were ready to sell out. That is all right as I will buy your things. But I think we can take some time yet. We don't know but things might change for the better.

Good-bye
Your loving father

Some of us folks may be down to see you before so long again.

CHAPTER 11

The Last Days in Military Camp

*E*ven though this was the second day John had spent resting in bed, physical weakness clung to him. With the afternoon sunlight streaming in through the window above his bed, he felt wrapped in gentle warmth, and soon a restful, healing sleep claimed him. Upon awaking, he was very hungry and reveled in the thought of joining the men in the mess hall that evening.

"It's great having you along again," Harvey said, as they walked through the crisp fall evening. "Sure gets lonely taking this same route each mealtime."

"Believe me, it feels great to be up and about. Um! Smells like beef stew! This walk and that smell surely have whetted my appetite!"

"Let's go pay the library a visit," Harvey suggested when they had finished eating.

"Well," John hedged, "care if I skip out? I think a walk and fresh air will do more for me than being cooped up in a stale library. I'm feeling even better since eating supper, and maybe if I have a good walk, I'll be able to sleep all night."

"Sure, I'm just thankful you are on the mend. Had me worried there for a while. I'll mosey over and pick up a book, then meet you back at our room," his friend replied as they parted company.

John turned his steps towards the stables, longing for something that provided more of a farm view than walking among the hundreds of barracks buildings. All the camp's barracks, except two, ran parallel to Route 104. One of these crossed Columbus Avenue where a farmhouse stood. The other was built perpendicular to an Indian Mound not far from John's quarters.

Guess I'll walk by the mound first, he told himself. *I've been intrigued by the information I've uncovered at the library about the Hopewell Indians, known as architects and builders of mounds. To think that many years ago people built these ancient mounds, which are scattered over southern Ohio! And they did not live at these earthworks, but built them as a cover for their burials!*

Stepping up to the mound, his mind replayed information he had gleaned from his research. These mounds were built in stages, with the first step being the construction of a wooden structure containing a clay platform where the dead were either cremated or buried on site. Buried with them were useful pottery, stone or copper implements, spearheads, and whatever else the Indians thought would be needed to protect and provide for them in the life hereafter. After many burial ceremonies the wooden structure was either burned or dismantled, and the entire area covered with a low mound of earth. This low mound was then covered by alternate layers of sand and earth, with the last being a thick layer of gravel and pebbles.

I wonder how many people are buried beneath this mound? he mused as he viewed the smooth mound surrounded by barracks. *Souls who died hundreds of years ago thought their bones and belongings would be protected by all this earth. Now I stand by this mound surrounded by men training for war. Thousands of men unprepared to die, putting their trust in guns, just as the Hopewell men felt safe being buried with their spearheads.*

John stood lost in thought. He would need to write and tell Ida all he knew. She would love hearing about them.

"Ha!" A harsh laugh startled John.

"Where is your Bible?" another soldier mocked.

"Aw, he's probably trying to resurrect the buried Indians so he can preach to them!" one said scornfully. Loud guffaws sent the group of five doubling over in mirth.

"Yellow! Chicken yellow!" the first assailant taunted. John recognized his antagonist. "Where you been lately? Hiding?" The soldier's eyes narrowed in disgust, and he spit on the ground at John's feet. "Answer me!" he demanded, his voice thick with fury as he grabbed John by the back of his uniform.

"I've been sick," John answered quietly.

"Sick! Hear that, boys? He's sick! And I tell you, you are sick!" he ground out each word through clenched teeth. "Sick? I should . . ."

"Baptize him!" the suggestion came with a peal of laughter.

"Yes!" the group took up the cry. "Here is a pump! Right over here is water. Let's baptize him good!" John felt himself picked up and thrust under a stream of cold water from the drinking fountain. His already chilled body reacted in shock to the cold water and cool night air. When he was thoroughly drenched, the group released him and mercifully left, leaving him numb with cold and his teeth chattering uncontrollably. John thought of Jesus' prayer on the cross when He faced his tormentors, "Father, forgive them; for they know not what they do."

By the time he returned to his barracks, his body no longer felt the cold. Since his request for his wallet or an extra blanket had continually been denied, the only clothes he had were the ones he was wearing. Taking off his wet clothes, he wrung out the water, redressed, and hoped they would dry before bedtime. That night his clothes were still damp, but as there was nothing else he could do, he left them on, wrapped himself in his blanket, and went to bed. Before morning the outdoor temperature plunged below freezing, and Camp Sherman awoke to find the ground covered with autumn's first frost.

When the morning bugle call rolled over camp, John could hardly make himself get up. Fever wracked him, leaving him shaky, and his cough had returned.

"John Witmer; Order Number 149," an army corporal called as he strode into the room. "You are to transfer to CO camp now," he ordered. "Take your belongings and walk." Turning on his heel, the officer left the barracks and disappeared outside.

"Praise God! I'm so glad!" Harvey rejoiced. "I've been praying you would be transferred soon."

"I hope you get your transfer today too," John said, clasping his friend's hand. John was too weak to say more or mention how bad he was feeling. Picking up his nearly empty suitcase, he started the walk to the CO camp. The mile seemed endless. Would he be able to walk that far? *Lord, give me strength,* he prayed.

He walked a short distance, stopped and rested on his

suitcase, walked some more, rested, prayed, walked, rested, prayed, but kept his focus on the haven of living among other Christians, until, finally, he reached camp.

By this time his head was swimming, his throat and tongue felt thick, and it hurt to cough. But a joy and thanksgiving flowed through him at the thought of being in the midst of friends.

Upon arrival at the CO camp, John stopped at headquarters to register. "You will be in Tent 94," said a pleasant-faced officer named Captain Hough. Captain Hough looked at John sharply, noting the unnatural flush of his face. "I suggest you have the camp doctor check you before going to your tent. You look like you're carrying a bug!" he chuckled.

"I have been under the weather," John confessed, glad to take his advice.

The doctor proved to be as kind as Captain Hough. After taking John's temperature, he questioned, "When did your fever start? Have you gotten chilled lately?"

Upon hearing about John's damp clothing, he asked in amazement, "Why in the world did you leave damp clothes on! That is the worst possible thing you could have done!"

"These are all the clothes I have, sir. My personal belongings were confiscated the day after I came."

The doctor's lips were set in a thin line. "You said your clothes got wet last night? By you or someone else?"

"I'll be fine now that I am here," John replied, evading his question.

The doctor made no comment but checked John's throat and tongue again and reached for some pills. "Take these right away. Gargle every morning and evening and try to rest the remainder of the day. Your tongue is coated with white, and that is not good."

John reveled in the tension-free quietness enveloping their primitive camp. It was indeed an oasis in the desert of hostility. He shared a tent with three Old Order Amish boys, and for the first time in nearly a week, he slept all night cocooned in the warmth of another blanket and the radiating love of brothers in Christ.

By morning the medicine had brought his fever down so he went along with some of the boys to pick apples at an orchard out in the country. Fallen leaves crunched under their shoes. Squirrels scampered up tree trunks, scolding profusely at being interrupted in their morning work by the invasion of the 160 intruders in their territory.

Winter is coming! Don't you know we must store up every good nut we can find? the squirrels seemed to say in their constant chatter. John embraced the outdoors, drinking in its beauty. But the two-mile walk to the orchard sapped his strength, and he felt too weak to work.

"Don't worry about helping," his tent mate, Joni, quickly assured him. "I think you should sit still and soak up the warm sunshine. That will be the best medicine for your cough."

"If I rest a little, maybe I can help later on," John whispered.

Joni had to lean forward to catch what John said. He watched with concern as John took a seat against the fence, then hunched forward, wrenched by a hollow, wracking cough from deep inside. Joni frowned. John should have stayed in camp. Joni waited until he saw John relax, then joined the other 158 workers who were busy picking fruit.

John did rest, lulled by the pleasant conversation and the steady thud of fruit being dropped into baskets. He imagined the trees singing with relief whenever a sagging branch was stripped bare of its bright red apples and bounced back to its pre-summer position. But by afternoon John's fever had returned. Joni insisted on accompanying him back to the camp doctor.

After checking his throat and taking his temperature, the doctor handed John a bottle. "Here is some more medicine I want you to take," he said. "Take some now and go to bed. You need rest to regain your strength."

John did as the doctor ordered, and soon he started coughing up mucus, which helped him breathe easier. Although he was worn out from the day's excursion, he felt the need to write home. Painstakingly he wrote in shaky handwriting:

I certainly enjoy the company better here than I did down in the other camp. There are three Old Order Amish boys in the same tent that I am. They are nice boys.

I did not get my clothes and my money yet. I did get your money order. The officer here told me I will be in this camp a few months at least so please send me the following things.

1 flashlight like you have at home and one extra battery. 1 folding drinking cup and some toothpicks, my singing book, 4 pr. Canvas gloves, 1 black shirt, a coat, vest and overcoat.

The next day Captain Hough himself visited John. "Take care," he admonished as he left.

Being in charge of these CO boys is definitely changing my attitude towards them, he thought. *Their submissive service is above reproach, and an inner happiness seems to govern their actions.* When he thought of the difference between the CO boys and the boys in training, he shook his head in wonder. *Their very lives testify to being content in serving their God! I thought they would tire and soon lose their "righteousness," but instead I find that, in spite of opposition, the boys are even more committed to doing what they believe is right! How do these boys spend their evenings? It is unbelievable, but they are perfectly content to talk, or sing, and they even get together to read their Bibles!*

Captain Hough found himself looking for opportunities to be with them. They drew him like a magnet, and he was glad to listen, observe, and find out more about this peculiar group of people.

CHAPTER 12

October 3, 1918

ear Cousin Walter,
I am still very weak. I can walk around and take care of myself but it goes hard to eat anything. I do not have any pain. The officers say my case is not dangerous. This disease is over the whole camp. I guess it is the Spanish Influenza. The officer says I am over the influenza and am only weak from the fever. The whole camp is quarantined. You can see that I cannot write as usual. I cannot use the pen now.

John's hand fell limp and his pen tumbled to the floor. Trembling with weakness, John lay exhausted, unable to move or call for help. He knew something was wrong, but had no strength to think about it. The letter was never finished.

While John lay in a senseless stupor, his family rejoiced to read that he was now in camp. "Praise God!" Mother expressed everyone's feelings. Her burden for her son's welfare lifted. He was no longer at the mercy of enemies.

Ida was delighted. She and Mary hurried through clean-up after supper so that they could write to John.

"Owen and I can mail it tomorrow on our way to school," Mary bubbled. "Then John will get it real quick!" She hurried to get paper and pen for Ida.

Harvey's father called up yesterday and said Harvey sent home for clothes. Are you quarantined yet? Mary wants me to write a little for her. She wants me to tell you that we put the white chickens in the henhouse yesterday evening. She likes to go to school. She likes her teacher. Wishing you God's richest blessing.

Your Sister
Ida Witmer

CHAPTER 13

Base Hospital

*S*unday morning a W.M.C.A. volunteer wrote the following letter:

Camp Sherman Ohio,

Your son is sick in base hospital. He ask me to write for him. He says he does not suffer much. He think the nurses are very kind.

He says he invites you to come as soon as you can to visit him and I will add to this that he is very sick and come if you can.

John M. Witmer
Base Hospital Ward 22
Camp Sherman

The same afternoon a telegram was sent to the family.

Mother's pulse quickened as Father gravely read the telegram aloud.

John M. Witmer. Very sick. Come immediately. Base Hospital

Dear son, Mother's heart wept. *What more will he have to suffer?* She longed to be his nurse. Didn't a mother's touch often bring healing?

"Dan, when do you think you can go?" she asked, her voice trembling.

"I'll plan to go tonight if possible. Maybe my brother John will be willing to go with me."

"Good! And I hope John *can* go with you," Mother said anxiously. "I feel an urgency."

"So do I," Father reflected solemnly.

While arrangements were being made to leave by train for the Base Hospital, Mother put together a box of food and home medical remedies she thought might help John. She longed to go with the men, but that was impossible. Instead, she drew strength and comfort by praying for her son.

That evening as Father told his wife and family good-bye, he reminded Mother, "Remember to call Frank Horst's neighbor in the morning and leave a message about John's sickness."

"Oh, yes! I wasn't thinking clearly. I will remember to do that."

After the breakfast dishes were finished Monday morning, Mother dialed the operator to put through the long distance call. Frank Horst belonged to the Old Order Team Mennonites, which did not use telephones. Only in an emergency did they bother their neighbors to deliver a message. Father and Mother felt the telegram from the hospital warranted a call. Her heart constricted at the implication.

"This is Anna Witmer calling. We received a telegram from Base Hospital, where John is a patient, and Dan felt we should get word to Nola," she explained when her call connected.

"I'll be glad to take over a message," came the reassuring answer.

"The telegram said John is very sick. Tell Nola that Dan and his brother John left last night on the train and should have gotten there around 8:00 this morning."

When her neighbor delivered the message, Nola was seized by fear. *John must be seriously sick for Witmers to call by phone and for Dan and his brother to have left for the hospital,* she thought.

"Thank you for telling me," she stammered in confusion, her mind reeling. What if John never made it home alive? She clasped her hands together, pausing to get her emotions under control. To think, her John lay sick, many miles away, and she could not go to him! It could well be she would never see him again! In a daze she stammered, "Thanks for coming over and telling me, it . . . it . . . means more than I can say," she said. Her words sounded hollow and far away.

"I know it is a shock, dear." Her motherly neighbor patted her arm sympathetically. "If I can be of any help, be sure and let me know."

"I'm glad his father is with him," Nola said and took a deep breath. "Could you pray for John? I . . . I . . . know it means a lot to him that we remember him," she added. "He said it was the prayers of his family and friends that helped him endure the time at military camp." Tears

97

threatened to spill from her shining dark eyes.

"I'll be glad to pray for John. And if you need to send a message, feel free to come over."

When her neighbor left, Nola stumbled to her bedroom where she buried her head in her arms and sobbed in anguish. "O Father, O Heavenly Father, You've called my dear mother to leave this world. Are you calling John home too? Must I lose another person dear to me? Oh, John! John! My Father in heaven, if it pleases Thee to answer my prayer, touch John and grant him health again. But if it is not Thy will . . ." She struggled with her own desire and to surrender all to Christ. In humble submission she gave John's life into the hands of her Father.

"I do want Thy will, Father. Be near to John; bless him and may he feel Your arms of love surrounding him." The cold fear that wanted to shake her faith dissipated as she took her fears to the Father.

All day Nola kept busy. She hardly noticed when dusk stole over the farm, for she seemed in another world. Mechanically she worked at folding Monday's wash. Della and Mary Ann cast sad glances at their sister but kept silent, sharing in her grief at John's sickness.

In what condition did Dan and his brother find John? How long would they stay? Was John improving? Or was he getting worse? Nola retired for the night with questions and thoughts of her beloved firmly entwined with precious memories of past times and talks and letters. Prayer drew her close to her beloved, and she slipped into a restful sleep.

CHAPTER 14

Monday Night,
October 7-8, 1918

"*P*apa!" The words were barely audible as John beheld his father. Gladness transformed his sunken eyes as he smiled up into the beloved face from home. "I . . . am . . . so . . . glad . . . you . . . came." Each word took labored effort to say.

Father clasped his son's thin hand, appalled at how wasted he was. With a wrenching cough, John sank back onto his pillow in exhaustion.

"Church." John mouthed, and his father bent down to catch what he was trying to say. "Preach. You preach?"

"Yes, son, I preached yesterday. It was my turn. I spoke on the choices we make."

"Tell me."

"Wrong choices bring discouragement and can be devastating. Do we have the vision to see down the road?" John relaxed as he listened to his father's voice. "The choices we make now may not affect us immediately, but later in life we will have to bear the impact those choices determine." He paused for it looked as though his son might have fallen asleep.

"Go . . . on," John's lips said, and he opened his eyes to look into his father's face.

"Do the choices we make and the path we take, lead us onward and upward in our walk with our Lord? In the beginning of creation when Adam and Eve doubted God's command not to eat of the tree of knowledge of good and evil, they heard, they doubted, and then they stayed on to listen. Think of what that wrong choice cost them!" Father forgot he was speaking to an audience of only one, for the intensity and hunger with which his son drank in every word stirred his pastor heart to fill the thirsty heart with spiritual nourishment.

"Son, we have Joseph who chose right when he left his coat and fled temptation. Enoch chose to walk with God. Noah chose to obey God and for 120 years he lived during a time when everyone else but his family went a different direction. His choice preserved not only his life, but also the lives of his family. Abraham left Hur, not knowing whither he went. He trusted God and went."

John closed his eyes, soothed by the healing balm of God's precious Word. He had sorely missed the preaching of the Word. His father's voice transported him back home, inside the doors of White Mennonite Church.

Father sensed John's need to hear the Word of God, and continued, "Then we have Lot, who chose to live where life was easy, where material gain became his god. He lost all, his family, even his wife. And lest we forget, we have Moses as an example. He chose to suffer affliction with the people of God rather than to enjoy the pleasures of sin for a season.

"All these men of faith had servant hearts. They chose to serve God, doing what He asked. Son, you made the right choice when you remained faithful and obedient to your Lord and Saviour at all costs."

John smiled peacefully.

"While I was studying for this message, a poem came to me, but I'll share it another time. I am afraid I am making you more tired."

John shook his head slowly. "No . . . it . . . will bless . . . my . . . heart," he whispered.

"Then I will quote it; then we will rest awhile," Father said.

> We have an open Bible,
> > Wherein is written clear,
> Commands for us to follow,
> > Its principles hold dear.
> Words of godly wisdom,
> > Which hold the keys of life,
> Written for generations,
> > A guide through daily strife.
> Examples we have to follow,
> > Give courage to face each test,
> Wherein is found The Way of Life,
> > For peace, joy, gladness, rest.

The low voices of nurses, the steps of people walking, muffled bumps of workers, moans and tossing of other patients, and John's labored breathing disrupted the quietness of the hospital.

"When . . . did . . . you get . . . the . . . message . . . I was . . . sick?" John whispered after rousing from rest.

"Late yesterday afternoon. I contacted Uncle John, and

we arranged to come on the night train," Father said, then reached to help John as he began another fit of coughing.

"I . . . have . . . not slept . . . since I . . . came . . . in." John's lips barely moved as he tried to whisper.

"Just sleep, son. Either Uncle John or I will stay with you at all times."

When night came, Father turned to his brother and said, "You should sleep. I will take care of John tonight."

All through the long night hours John's father kept a vigil at his bedside. A nurse brought a rubber bottle filled with ice, which Father kept on his son's forehead in hopes of bringing down his fever. Whenever John moaned or stirred, Father offered him water. As his son fought to breathe, Father prayed for strength to accept God's will for their son. Unless God touched him with a miracle, John could not live much longer. "Not my will, but thine be done," his father prayed as dawn dispelled another night and morning sunrise spread across Camp Sherman.

Back in Columbiana, the Witmer family knelt in prayer, beseeching God's mercy and healing for their beloved brother and son. Harvest was still in progress, school started at 8:30, the horses needed to be fed and watered, and it was time to bring in the parsnips so that the garden would be ready to plow. Work did not stop with Father gone and John in the hospital.

"I'm sure glad we got John's ground disked and wheat planted before Father left," Enos said, turning toward Mother. "Now Ezra and I can concentrate on harvesting corn. If all goes well, we should finish the north field today."

"Will Father be home tonight?" Owen asked.

"That depends on how John is doing, but I hope he is," Mother said, giving the only answer she herself clung to.

Nola, too, filled her day with the daily tasks of keeping house for her family. Again and again her heart became burdened for her loved one, and she found solace on her knees, at the feet of Jesus. Heaviness of spirit, yet sweet peace, enveloped her as she waited for further word.

At Base Hospital, the two brothers again kept vigil beside John's bedside. He did not seem to get any worse during the day, but remained basically the same. Very few words were exchanged between the three, for each time John tried to say something, he ended up coughing. As long as Father and Uncle John stayed at his bedside, he seemed content to rest.

That evening his breathing became shallower, and John lay as in a coma. "I believe John's life on earth is almost finished," Father said to Uncle John. How thankful Father was that his brother was here with him in these last moments of parting. At 11:00 P.M., God called John home, and his spirit fled to meet his Maker. Never again would John need to suffer. His work on earth was finished.

"It is just a little over four weeks since John received his notice from our earthly country to report for duty on September the 6th. Now he has received his call from God to report to his heavenly country," Father said as he held the lifeless hand of his son. Though tears coursed unheeded down his cheeks, his heart was at peace with his heavenly Father's decision.

"John faced many tests since he left home. Some we know about, and there are probably many others we will never know," said Uncle John. "I have to think, Dan, it is a joy to know he passed the final test. His reward is eternal life." Uncle John laid a comforting hand on his brother's shoulder.

"I was shocked when I saw how wasted his body was,"

Father replied. "I feel he has suffered far more physically than he ever wrote home."

"I believe so too," his brother reflected. "I will miss my namesake, but we have no doubt that John was ready to go. You know, when man called John to report for duty, he could not conscientiously fulfill that duty. I believe at the same time man called, God called him to report for duty, the duty of remaining faithful even if he needed to suffer. Brother Dan, I feel confident John fulfilled that duty."

"Thank you, brother, for the encouragement. Though we sorrow, it is not without hope of someday joining him. Now I must see if I can get word to Anna. I think a telegram will be the surest way of getting word to her by morning. I hope we can be on the train home by that time."

CHAPTER 15

October 9, 1918

$\mathcal{M}$ other held the telegram in her hand. The words blurred as she read.

John died. 11:00 P.M. Arrive 10th with body.

My son, my son, her heart cried, as she clasped the telegram with shaking hands. As if in a dream, she sank into a kitchen chair, clutching the bit of paper. Her first-born! She had nursed him, taught him and cared for him. She had watched and prayed for him as he grew from babyhood to manhood. She could still remember the joy enveloping her when he had responded to God's call for salvation. She saw him embracing the faith, reading and studying in the evenings when he could. She rejoiced in his quiet gentleness. He loved people, and he loved working with animals.

She knew he would someday leave home, but she had

always envisioned him leaving to set up housekeeping at his farm. But now, he was never returning! Her mother love had been cruelly stabbed. She wasn't prepared. She hadn't expected his life to end so quickly. Dropping her head onto the table, she poured out her grief and pain to God, her Father, who understood all.

In the stillness of the kitchen, Anna experienced the divine presence of God. It was as if He spoke audibly, for in her heart she plainly heard His voice reminding her, *I loved your son. I died for him, ". . . and (he) overcame him by the blood of the Lamb, and by the word of (his) testimony; and (he) loved not (his life) unto the death. Therefore rejoice, ye heavens . . ."*

Anna wept, but was comforted to know her son was now in glory. Getting her Bible she turned to John 14 and began reading. "Let not your heart be troubled: ye believe in God, believe also in me."

"Yes, Father, I do believe," she whispered.

"In my Father's house are many mansions: if it were not so, I would have told you. I go to prepare a place for you." And John is there! A healing balm to read of Your love for us. *"And if I go and prepare a place for you, I will come again, and receive you unto myself; that where I am, there ye may be also."* Someday they would see John again! Morning sunlight danced through the window, bathing Anna with external warmth and light, just as God's Word wrapped her heart in blessed peace. She closed her Bible, praising God that her son had counted it joy to suffer for Christ.

Calmness and inner strength composed her, and she felt ready to tell the children of their brother's passing. She saw Ida and the boys returning from the barn and heard Mary descending the stair steps. "Help me, Lord, to comfort the children." She rose to welcome them with a sweet smile of resignation.

"Poor Nola, I know she loved John as much as we do," Ida said, weeping.

"I must call the Horst neighbors again and let Nola know of the telegram. Remember to pray for her today, God bless her dear heart," Mother said as she wiped her tears, longing to comfort the motherless girl who held such a special place in their family.

Father's grieving heart found solace in writing a poem of remembrance as he waited for the military to release John's body.

In Memory
of our
Son and Brother
John M. Witmer
died
October 8th 1918
aged
21 years, 5 months, 18 days

There was a time of deep distress
When sorrow all our hearts did press
They called a dear one from our home
In uniform to make him roam.
      They tried his faith with awful threat
      And led him toward the bayonet
      He read the Word before the throng
      In silence, beneath the noonday sun.
The letters that our loved one wrote
Gave evidence of his strong hope.
To gain a city bright and fair
Where there will be no cross to bear.

> Unto God we prayed for his care
> That they no more would keep him there
> That in his faith he would not waver
> But trust in Jesus our Saviour.

They saw the power of God at last
And left him be with the steadfast
With those who too had braved the storm
No more with those in uniform.

> The faithful now could worship there
> And sing to God and have sweet prayer
> To help a farmer they might go
> Where the luscious apples grow.

At length his health began to fail
His voice grew faint his cheek grew pale
From those who were at his bedside
There came a message he had died.

> His body rests beneath the sod
> His soul has gone home to God.
> He is forever now at rest
> No earthly foe can him molest.

While Father penned the poem, Nola faced her own personal agony of accepting the will of God. Her future hopes and dreams lay shattered, crushed, as ashes without any possibility of rebuilding. In the midst of her sorrow she clung to the everlasting promise: "My grace is sufficient for thee."

As word spread through her community, Nola gratefully welcomed the love and sympathy her church family extended by coming to share in her sorrow.

Father and Uncle John continued to have difficulty getting the release for John's body. "I thought we would get an immediate release once the doctor signed the death certificate," Father lamented. "I never thought the military would claim his body, but, it's true, he hadn't yet been interviewed by the Board of Inquiry of Conscientious Objectors. How would you feel if we just accompanied the body home when it goes?"

"I would be glad to do that," his brother agreed.

With a heavy heart, Father watched as John's body was placed in a military casket and draped with the American flag before being loaded onto a livery wagon. He knew the Spanish Influenza was sweeping through camp, and John's casket was only one of many being taken to the train depot. A military band marched in front of the wagons playing funeral hymns as the wagons wound their way through the streets of Chillicothe. Once the caskets were loaded onto the train, the band struck up the lively tune of "Dixie."

"Now why would they play that?" Father exclaimed, shaking his head in disbelief.

"Well, mister," said a man beside Father on the platform, "death isn't something we like. It lifts our spirits to hear a foot-tapping tune. Makes us forget the Grim Reaper."

Unknown to those gathered at the train depot, this was just the beginning of a widespread epidemic of death from the Spanish Influenza. By the end of October, 1,177 deaths were confirmed from Camp Sherman alone. Soldiers were dying in such numbers that the local theatre was used as a temporary morgue, and bodies were stacked like cordwood until caskets could be finished.

Since Father and Uncle John had left home Sunday evening, the state of Ohio had begun enforcing a quarantine of all public meeting places, including schools and churches, in an effort to stop the deadly epidemic from spreading.

Theatre used as temporary morgue

Hours later on the train home, Father remembered the letter handed to him as he left Camp Sherman. Pulling it from his coat pocket he opened it.

Conscientious Objector's Detachment,
158th Depot Brigade,
Camp Sherman, Ohio,
October 9, 1918

From: O. Conscientious Objector's Detachment.
To: O. 158th Depot Brigade, Camp Sherman, Ohio.
Subject: Clothing deceased Conscientious Objector.
         1. Pvt. John M. Witmer, 3857538, a Conscientious Objector's Detachment, was a sincere conscientious objector.
         2. He refused to wear the uniform or to accept non-combatant service but had not, as yet,

been interviewed by the Board of Inquiry on Conscientious Objectors; therefore, his status was not determined at the date of his death, 11:00 o'clock P.M. October 9, 1918.

3. Instructions from the Adjutant General's Office dated July 30th, 1918 provide that conscientious objectors shall not be required to wear the uniform pending final disposition of their case.

4. I, therefore, believe it advisable to bury this man in his civilian clothes.

R. J. Hough,
Captain Infantry U.S.A.
Condg.

RJH / VCM

1st Ind.

Hdqrs. 158th Depot Brigade, Camp Sherman, Ohio, October 9, 1918.

To: C.O. Conscientious Objector's Detachment, Camp Sherman, Ohio.

   1   Approved.

By order of COLONEL CUSACK

Hq., Camp Sherman, Ohio, October 9th, 1918.
Approved. By order of Colonel Rivers:

James F. C. Duvall	James M. Dromey
Major, A.C.D., Camp Adjt.	Captain Infantry U.S.A.
	Asst. Brig. Adjt.]

"Here, read this," said Father. "It is a great consolation. I had worried that the military might prevent us from having a civilian funeral." He handed the letter to his brother.

"Especially since a soldier accompanied his body on the train."

"Praise God for His goodness," said Uncle John. "This letter confirms without a shadow of a doubt the testimony your son left. I will pray that his suffering for Christ will bring conviction to men he had contact with. May souls be won for Christ's kingdom."

CHAPTER 16

October 10, 1918

*C*olumbiana's newspaper included a notice of the death of John M. Witmer, and the arrival of his body on the Pennsylvania R.R. October 10th with a military escort. This public announcement drew a crowd of local townspeople to meet the train. Some were acquaintances of the Witmer family, while others were curious spectators grabbing the opportunity to be at a public gathering. People were feeling the isolation since the Spanish Influenza epidemic sweeping the nation closed all public meeting places, including churches.

Out of respect for John's family, the crowd hung back, letting Anna, the siblings, and Uncle John's wife stand closest to the tracks. Brakes hissing, the train jerked to a stop and a hush descended when a soldier stepped down from the train. With a click of heels he stood at attention, his hand raised in salute while the flag-draped casket was lowered to a waiting cart. Mother's mouth dropped open, a wounded cry escaping her lips before she was able to stop it. *Do we have to bear this pain too?* her mind reeled in shock. *To see our son returned with military honors!*

"Mama!" Ida whispered in confusion, "Why did they send him home like that!"

Numbly, Mother shook her head, unable to answer. In silence the crowd watched as Father descended from the train. Mother caught his look of surprise as he hesitated momentarily, then he walked over to the casket and reached for the flag. Without a word he lifted off the symbol of patriotism, and folded it as he would have folded a blanket. His son did not die a soldier in the army. The flag was a mockery to all John Witmer suffered. He died serving his Master, Jesus Christ.

To the townspeople, the flag held the truest symbol of loyalty and honor. To see Dan Witmer folding the flag in such a common manner angered them. Didn't this man know he was desecrating the flag by not folding it according to code? The soldier heard the ripple of dissension, but reentered the train. He had fulfilled his duty. Let the town deal with this problem.

"Mennonites!" someone said disgustedly. The mood of the onlookers turned from one of sympathy to hostility.

"Got what he deserved," another added quickly.

"Traitor!" someone hissed.

A stone struck Enos on the shoulder, and another landed at Father's feet. Mary started to cry. In her innocence, she couldn't understand why anyone would want to hurt them.

John! Ida's heart cried. *What must you have had to endure!* She shivered as she thought of her brother and Harvey among thousands of such enemies.

"I didn't mean to stir up strife or show disrespect,"

Father apologized to the train station manager. "I did not know the flag had to be handled in a certain way, or I would have been happy to do it that way. I am truly sorry the people thought I was retaliating. We believe the Bible teaches us to serve God, to do good to all men, and to love everyone. We cannot take part in any patriotic activities because our allegiance is to God in heaven."

"They'll forget," the manager replied with a shrug.

"I need to stop at the funeral home and let them know we are taking the body home with us and will have the funeral the day after tomorrow," Father told the family as they prepared to leave the depot.

"Would you want me to leave word with the other ministers about what time to come over to your place?" Uncle John asked. "That way you will have some time alone with your family. I do feel you all need that," he finished kindly.

"Yes, thank you," Father said gratefully.

In the comfort and quiet of their living room, Father shared the last days he had spent with John. "We do not understand why God called him home, but the evening before he died, as he lay laboring for each breath, I was reminded how he had written home, 'We never know one minute what will happen the next.'"

Cleansing tears flowed as the family recalled the events of the past month.

"Harvey, who was also in CO camp, said John was abused more than he was. He said John felt it was because he had been baptized only a short time before the draft called him. Whatever the reason, we do not know for sure, but we do know John was faithful. He asked me to share the last sermon I preached, and I ended up preaching it again," Father wiped his eyes and blew his nose.

"Children, he seemed to drink in every word. I'm so

glad I was given the opportunity! He seemed satisfied afterwards just to rest. I wouldn't ask God to restore his life if it were possible. He looked so peaceful when he took his last breath. And now we know he is where there is no more pain or death."

The family gathered around the pine coffin, viewing the remains of their loved one. His thin, worn face and shaved head spoke of suffering.

"John is now seeing 'a city which hath foundations, whose builder and maker is God,'" Father quoted reverently.

CHAPTER 17

October 12, 1918

*A*utumn's resplendent color helped temper the cool dampness shrouding the small gathering of church friends and family who met for the funeral on the front lawn.

"Dearly beloved," said Brother Martin Ramer from Goshen, Indiana, as he looked out over the standing audience, "today we are called by God's appointment to attend this service. If we could have had our way, we would not have chosen that the life of a young man in his prime be snuffed out. But God had a purpose. Hebrews 9:27 reads, 'And as it is appointed unto men once to die, but after this the judgment.' John's appointment came October 8th at 11:00 P.M.

"Brothers and sisters, we have not as yet been given our appointments. Someone may receive his or hers today, or tomorrow. Life is uncertain; we have no promise of tomorrow. Let us now sing."

The sorrowing family perceived God's abiding presence in the message of the songs. It soothed like a healing balm, drawing each one's thoughts heavenward as the notes floated out from under the spreading maple trees and drifted upward to the sky overhead.

> Weep not for me my parents dear,
> Since I must go and leave you here.
> With Jesus I shall happy be.
> O parents, do not weep for me.

> Nearer my God to Thee,
>   Nearer to Thee;
> E'en though it be a cross
>   That raiseth me;
> Still all my song shall be,
>   Nearer my God, to Thee,
> Nearer to Thee.

Where is Nola? Why isn't she here? Ida wondered. She grew panicky as the service progressed, and Nola failed to arrive. *Hadn't Pricilla and Amos met Nola and her father at the station? Why are they here without her? Is she sick with the influenza too? Oh, I hope not! Several families from our congregation are under quarantine, but please, not Nola!*

Dear, dear Nola, Ida agonized as she thought of the pain Nola must be experiencing at not being able to attend John's funeral. *Lord, help her to bear the disappointment of missing out in this service. Comfort her, Lord, and thank You that I have been able to say good-bye to my brother's body. Seeing him again has helped me so much.* Ida wept, not only for herself, but also for Nola, because she would never have the opportunity to bid her John farewell.

When John's short funeral service ended, friends and neighbors offered words of comfort before returning to their homes. It was hardly safe to congregate in the outdoors. *Whose funeral would be next?* was the unspoken question lingering in their midst.

Back on the Horst farm Nola voiced her uneasiness when the family sat down to a bowl of soup for dinner. "Father, I'm almost sure John's funeral was to be today."

"You must have misunderstood. The message came through our neighbors, and they would know," he said, giving his daughter a sympathetic smile. "Keep busy today, daughter. The day will soon be over and tomorrow will be here. Then we will take the first train east."

He had buried his own beloved wife, and he understood Nola's suffering, yet he did not know what else to say to ease her heartache. Time. In time her pain would dull and disappear. No doubt she needed to see his face once more, to say good-bye, to see John's body buried. Then healing could begin. That was the way it had been for him.

Nola forced herself to keep busy. A measure of relief came when night arrived, for in the morning she would see John.

But as Nola and her father stepped from the train near Columbiana, bewilderment and doubt rushed over her. No one was there to meet them. They had expected someone from the church to be waiting. It wasn't quite 9:00; surely they would have expected her to come on the first train!

"Let's walk to the General Store," her father suggested, but before they reached the store, a horse and buggy pulled over beside them and stopped. Oh, such a relief! Someone had come! Nola recognized Amos Wenger and his sister.

"We were so sorry that you were sick yesterday," Pricilla said as Nola came up to the buggy.

"Sick?" she exclaimed, her face showing her bafflement. "I wasn't sick."

"But." Pricilla stammered, "you weren't at John's funeral. We all thought you were sick."

Nola turned ashen and would have fallen had not her father steadied her by the arm. "It can't be true!" she gasped brokenly as crushing disappointment enveloped her.

No! her mind screamed. *He can't be buried!*

A great cloud of darkness closed in, and Nola grabbed for the buggy seat, sinking against it. In seconds her head cleared, and she understood. Their neighbor had given the wrong information! It was true! She would never see John's beloved face again. She could not say good-bye. She had missed the funeral, the preaching, and the comfort of sharing her sorrow with others.

Numbly she climbed into the buggy. Sobbing silently, she buried her face in her hands. *Lord Jesus. My Father, be with me*, her heart cried.

"Could you take us out to Daniels?" Nola heard her father ask. "When Nola and I were leaving yesterday to catch the train, our neighbor met us at the end of the lane and asked where we were going. When I said where we were going, she told us the funeral wasn't until today. So Nola and I returned home."

"Nola, I am so very sorry," her father said, offering the only sympathy he knew. Pricilla squeezed her hand and everyone fell silent. Nola was grateful for the quiet as she struggled to accept this new disappointment.

Nola battled the tempter until she channeled her

thoughts heavenward. It was then that she could give her disappointment to God, and His peace restored her soul. *Maybe I thought too much of John, and God chose to remind me that nothing must come between Him and me.*

Those were almost the very words John had written in one of his letters when he was receiving harsh treatment. "I feel God is reminding me that nothing must come between Him and me." She recalled the joy that filled her to know her chosen was putting faith in God above all else.

My Father in heaven, help me to keep my eyes on Thee. John is in a better place. I don't want to resent that I missed bidding him good-bye. Someday I will see him again. I will lay hold on that promise. I praise Thee for answering my prayer, for giving me a peace that passeth all understanding. Nola gathered strength to accept her bitter cup and asked God to make her a blessing to John's family that day.

When they reached John's home, Mother held Nola in her arms as they wept together. Ida and Mary joined them as they walked to the grave. Once again tears flowed as they recounted John's last days on earth, grateful that John had chosen "rather to suffer affliction with the people of God, than to enjoy the pleasures of sin for a season."

They shed healing tears of love, reminding each other that God's love was greater than man's. Their tears also became tears of understanding and acceptance, knowing that John had been called to duty, and had not failed.

"We want you to have this," Mother said, as she gave Nola the Testament John had received the day he left for Camp Sherman.

Several days later Nola clipped John's obituary from the local newspaper a neighbor brought. Tears spilled down her cheeks as she read the final words.

John M. Witmer was born near Columbiana, Ohio. He was the oldest son of Daniel C. and Anna Witmer. He had always worked at home at farming until on September 6th, 1918 when he was called to Camp Sherman to take part in the U.S. Army, but being a conscientious objector he passed through some severe trials the first two weeks of camp, but he kept his faith.

When at camp about three weeks his health began to fail, which developed into pneumonia. On the 6th of October his parents received a telegram stating his illness. His father and uncle John went to his bedside and remained there until October 8th at 11 P.M. when he passed away; then they accompanied the body home arriving on October 10th.

He is survived by his parents, three brothers (Enos, Ezra, and Owen) two sisters (Ida and Mary) He united with the Mennonite Church on June 8, 1917 and remained a faithful member until death.

Funeral services were held at his late home on October 12th at 10 A.M. conducted by Bros. Martin Ramer of Goshen, Ind. and Moses Horst and Abram Good of Wadsworth, Ohio, text Hebrews 11:10 with burial at the White Mennonite Church near his home.

With trembling hands Nola placed the obituary with her beloved's letters. Giving up was not easy. Though her heart felt torn and bleeding, she rested in the assurance that God had her life in His control.

CHAPTER 18

After John's Death

aniel Witmer and family;   *Severn*
                                           S.C.
                                           Oct. 12, 1918

Dear folks:

I had a card from Phares Witmer last evening stating John's death at Camp Sherman. I indeed was sorry to hear it, but trust that he is now where we all expect to be someday. You folks have my deepest sympathy.

                          From Walter Martin

"How thoughtful!" Father said after reading the letter to the family. "He is encouraging us because we are brothers in Christ."

Within eight weeks of John's death, the Spanish Influenza had also claimed the lives of two young women from the White Church. The one was buried only weeks before she was to be married. As Nola viewed her dressed in her wedding dress, her own fresh sorrow wanted to overwhelm her.

"Without God's grace and power, we could not accept these tragedies," she testified to the grieving "bridegroom."

It was bittersweet news when the war ended, November 11, 1918. The day the Armistice was signed was one month and three days after John's death. *Why, Lord. Why?* The unanswered question surfaced repeatedly to plague Nola, sometimes when she least expected it. Again and again she needed to turn to God's Word for comfort, assurance, and faith.

Time moved on. Days slipped into weeks, and the weeks turned into months. Then one day, Jake Miller, an Amish man who was one of the first three conscientious objectors at CO camp at Camp Sherman, wrote to the Dan Witmer family.

"John did not die in vain," he penned. "I want to tell your family that Captain Hough was converted to Christianity. He said it was because of the testimony of the Amish and Mennonite boys at camp. Through them he became convinced that Jesus Christ is the only way to peace."

More years sped by. John's mother, Anna, passed away August 2, 1947, and his father, Dan, July 15, 1966. Both were laid to rest beside their son. They went home to meet John in that city not made with hands.

The years continued. One day, Brother Israel Snyder, a minister of White Mennonite Church, answered a knock at his door. Before him stood a well-dressed, white-haired man, years older than he.

"I have come to make something right," the stranger

said. "In 1918 I was a soldier training in Camp Sherman. Am I correct that the late John Witmer was a member of your church?" he asked hesitantly.

"Yes, he was. I was not a minister then, but I know who you are talking about," Brother Israel answered, his curiosity aroused.

"Then maybe you would also have heard of his mistreatment while in camp?" The man shifted from one foot to the other.

"Yes, I have," Israel assured him.

"What I need to confess is this: I feel I am the one that sent John Witmer to his death. Several days before he died, he was soaked with cold water. I was the one that turned the cold water onto him and made sure he was completely soaked. I knew he had no other clothes to change into. I also knew he had only one blanket, and with our unheated barracks it got pretty cold by morning.

"I hated him then. After the war ended, I had no hatred, but I have carried this guilt for years. John was not physically strong, but his unbending steadfastness to do right infuriated me. He condemned me by his inner strength. I had no inner strength, only outward bullying," he said. Tears of remorse shone in his eyes as he recalled the tragedy of those bygone days.

"Could you, would you find someone in his family and tell them that I have asked God for forgiveness? God in his great mercy has forgiven me my sins, and I am asking them to forgive me for my cruel actions and for the suffering I brought to the family. I feel the need to confess before men so that when my time is up, I am ready to meet John in eternity," he said, his voice husky with emotion.

"Certainly, brother, I will be happy to relay your request. And I rejoice that you have taken care of your soul's need while there is still time. John's parents are gone, but I believe I would know someone who can direct me to where his sister lives. I feel certain none of the family has held ill feelings towards anyone. But they will appreciate hearing that John did not give his life in vain, and that you have heeded the call of God for your salvation. May God bless you as you continue to follow his leading." Brother Israel clasped the hand of the man before him.

"Thank you," the forgiven man responded fervently. "I am now at peace."

Later Brother Israel shared the ex-soldier's confession with Ida, whose snow-white hair spoke of the many years that had passed since girlhood. "We all have weaknesses and need forgiveness," she responded promptly. "I never held any animosity for my brother's tormenters, only sorrow. I feel sorry for the man who carried the guilt of John's death for all these years. But I rejoice that he has found peace. It makes me wonder how many other lives John touched that we know nothing about."

As Ida watched the young minister walk away, the words from Matthew 5 rose to her lips.

> Blessed are the pure in heart: for they shall see God.
>
> Blessed are the peacemakers: for they shall be called the children of God.
>
> Blessed are they which are persecuted for righteousness' sake: for theirs is the kingdom of heaven.
>
> Blessed are ye, when men shall revile you, and persecute you, and shall say all manner of evil against you falsely, for my sake.
>
> Rejoice, and be exceeding glad: for great is your

reward in heaven: for so persecuted they the prophets which were before you.

John, dear brother John! Ida's thoughts traveled back through time, and a smile spread across her face as she recalled God's words of promise that had sustained her as a young girl. *Blessed are they that do his commandments, that they may have right to the tree of life, and may enter in through the gates into the city.**

* Revelation 22:14

Christian Light Publications, Inc., is a nonprofit, conservative Mennonite publishing company providing Christ-centered, Biblical literature including books, Gospel tracts, Sunday school materials, summer Bible school materials, and a full curriculum for Christian day schools and homeschools. Though primarily produced in English, some books, tracts, and school materials are also available in Spanish.

For more information about the ministry of CLP or its publications, or for spiritual help, please contact us at:

Christian Light Publications, Inc.
P. O. Box 1212
Harrisonburg, VA 22803-1212

Telephone—540-434-0768
Fax—540-433-8896
E-mail—info@clp.org